Chaos
in the kitchen =
Symmetry
at
the
table

Published by
MOUNTAINAIR PRESS
for
THE ASPEN CENTER FOR PHYSICS

MountainAir

Chaos in the Kitchen = Symmetry at the Table

Editors: Beate Block and Maggie DeWolf
Recipes: Physicists and their friends from around the world
Type Design: Steve Lundeen
Typography: Jennifer Voight and Meri Pincock-Hause
Art Directed and Created by: SS. Burrus and Diane Christoffel-Voight
Cover Design: Diane Christoffel-Voight

Ordering Information:
    The Aspen Center for Physics
    700 West Gillespie Street
    Aspen, Colorado 81611 USA
    Telephone: 1-970-925-2585
        Fax: 1-970-920-1167
      E-Mail: jane@aspenphys.org

Published by MountainAir Press and the Aspen Center for Physics.

Printed in the United States of America

ISBN# 0-929526-18-X

TABLE OF CONTENTS

EDITORS'S NOTE

This is not a conventional cookbook. We invite you to look through it for interesting recipes and to think of it as a contribution that science has made to the fine arts and craft of cooking.

SS. BURRUS

THE ASPEN CENTER FOR PHYSICS

The Aspen Center for Physics was started in 1962 by Bob Craig, Mike Cohen and George Stranahan as part of the Aspen Institute of Humanistic Studies. Its purpose was then and is today to be a research center where physicists can work in an unstructured environment, allowing them to be free to interact across their fields of specialization. In 1968 the Center became the independent, non-profit organization that it is today and includes experimental and theoretical physicists, biophysicists and biologists. The Center sponsors individual research, summer workshops, winter conferences and a variety of outreach lectures and programs in the Roaring Fork Valley.

ACKNOWLEDGMENTS

56 .BURRUS

TO: Martin Block for his inspiration and encouragement and his love of good food, good wine and the sharing with good friends.

TO: Nick DeWolf for his suggestions and his desire to feed the world with food that tastes good.

TO: Jane Kelly of the real world, Administrative Vice President of Aspen Center for Physics and provider of help and advice when the going got tough.

TO: Diane Christoffel-Voight for her artistic insights, her good cheer and her interest in bringing the world of physics to the Roaring Fork Valley.

TO: Deb Pease, Financial Director of the Aspen Center for Physics, whose expertise has kept us solvent and who gave us the only recipe truly unique to the Rocky Mountains.

TO: Steve Lundeen for "webster", the font for our book and for answering the innumerable questions we had.

TO: Last, but not least, the anonymous tasting committee who has been game to try it all!

BIOGRAPHIES

Beate Block, who has compiled the recipes in this book, is the wife of a physicist and an experienced cook. She has spent many years living abroad and attending particle physics conferences throughout the world with her husband. Bea now lives year-round in Aspen, Colorado with Martin who is Professor Emeritus of Physics and Astronomy at Northwestern University, Evanston, Illinois. The Blocks are life-long devoted skiers and Martin is a fly fisherman of consummate skill who fishes trout streams in Colorado today as he fished salmon streams in Europe over the past many years. Martin is a member of the Aspen Center for Physics and founder of the Winter Physics Conferences, sponsored by the Center and now in their 16th year.

Maggie DeWolf, co-editor of this book, lives in Aspen, Colorado with her husband Nick and with numerous cats and dogs. Nick and Maggie are both members of the Aspen Center for Physics and Nick is the designer and builder of the Aspen Fountain which dances in the mall during the summer. Maggie tends a substantial garden in the summer and promotes physics lectures in the winter. The DeWolf house has provided many memorable feasts throughout the years for visiting physicists and their families.

Diane Christoffel-Voight, whose illustrations enliven this cookbook, was born, raised and educated in America's Dairyland on the shores of Lake Michigan. Since leaving Wisconsin some 30 years ago and coming to the Roaring Fork Valley, Diane and her husband Tom have settled in New Castle, Colorado with horses, dogs and cats and raised two children. They are the founders of Wintercount, a publishing company of Native American Art, pictured on greeting cards and calendars. Through the years, Diane has tripled many a recipe to satisfy hungry physicists and her artistic posters for the Winter Conferences are a feast for the eyes.

Our second illustrator is SS (SamSam) Burrus of Santa Fe, New Mexico where she is a member of the Paint Clan of the Cherokee Indian Nation. Sam is a writer, poet and artist, as well as illustrator and we feel privileged to present her work in our cookbook. We think her drawings add a whimsical dimension to our recipes and perhaps a touch of magic to the food.

Introduction
by GRACE MARMOR SPRUCH

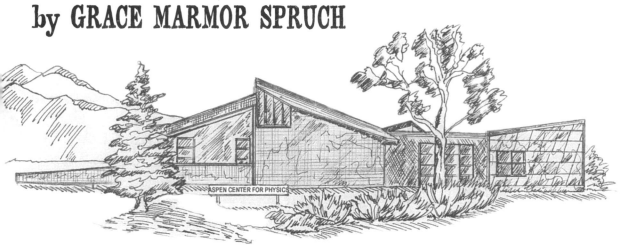

In the beginning, there was Tom's Market. There was also Beck and Bishop's, but where City Market now stands there was only a void.

The beginning was 1962, the year The Aspen Center for Physics opened with a small bang. The Aspen Institute for Humanistic Studies and the Aspen Music Festival had been in operation for more than a decade. In fact, the Physics Center was built on Aspen Institute land and was named the Physics Division of the Aspen Institute for Humanistic Studies. But this isn't a history of the Physics Center; it's the story of the Physics Center as digested through the stomachs of a few. That is, it's the Physics Center as it relates to food, the eating kind, though in describing some aspects of the Aspen that used to be, we might, provide some food for thought - if not indigestion.

The twenty or so (total of forty-five for the summer) intrepid pioneers that first year were housed in houses, not condos, in town. There may have been some condos in Aspen then but the physicists were not conscious of them. Small as the houses were, by today's Aspen standards, they obeyed Bose Einstein statistics in accommodating infinite numbers by having every surface larger than a chair convertible to a bed. Several still stand, one on the corner of Third and Francis.

There was no mall, no huge Ritz Carlton-St. Regis type of hotel, only the pre-refurbished shabbily majestic Jerome, with a pool where the patio now stands. The pool featured topless swimming some time in the seventies according to several Physics Center observers. To swim and shower cost $1.75, to just shower cost 75 cents. The latter was of great importance to the young backpackers coming down from the mountains after a week away from civilization. One member of the Physics Center lost his underwear to one of these. At least, he <u>hoped</u> it was lost to a backpacker rather than to the trash basket in the shower room - such was the condition of the underwear. The public pool on Maroon Creek Road didn't exist, nor did the city tennis courts on Maroon Creek Road. Tennis was played on the asphalt courts of the former elementary school in town. Dee Dee, the past very popular tennis pro who directed the City's tennis program and instructed many of the "Fizzies", as she called them, existed, but wasn't old enough to play tennis.

The hot spot in town the first years was the Red Onion, which featured a weekly "Twist" contest one year. A very reclusive, quite distinguished, eminently unlikely field theorist revealed that he could do the twist. He was promptly assured that should he enter the contest he would win, as the entire Center would be rounded up to applaud. (skill was measured by the intensity of audience response.) However, shyness triumphed over arguments invoking a mother's pride in her offspring's achievement. But our subject is food.

The only public "food" event the first year was a kind of political cocktail party organized by a physics wife who had worked for the noted civil rights leader James Farmer, who was at the Aspen Institute that summer. He came to the cocktail party to field questions the physicists might toss at him.

The Physics Center had close ties to the Aspen Institute for several of the early years, the Center regularly supplying physicists to give lectures "for the public" at the Institute. Supporting these efforts spiritually, if not financially, was Robert O. Anderson, a local multimillionaire, affectionately named 10^8* Anderson, by the physicists, after his reported net worth. What did 10^8* have to do with food? A tiny bit. He too was housed in town, in an old Victorian he owned, and his legacy extended to lending his Jeep -- one of about five vehicles parked outside his house to some of the physicists. One graduate student wanted to borrow the Jeep for a near-inaccessible hike, but was terrified he might damage it. He was reassured when it was pointed out to him that even if he were to total it, the cost of the Jeep to Anderson was in the same ratio as a stick of gum to his, the grad student's total assets.

Some years after the beginning, when the center's activities were still opaque, Maurice became visible. Maurice was the chef at the Aspen Alps restaurant. He had been apprenticed at age thirteen in the household of one of the Rothchilds. In Aspen, considerably older than thirteen, in addition to running the restaurant, he moonlighted by giving "cooking classes" in the kitchen. A few enterprising members of the Physics Center would round up about a dozen people for a "class", which consisted of a six course (with wines) lecture demonstrated by Maurice, resplendent in chef's toque and apron, armed with his trusty measuring cup (half an egg shell), the chefs knife he wielded as the fastest chopper in the west - no cuisinart for him! - (Just don't 'av the knife rise higher than the knuckles") and an arsenal of French accented jokes. Each dish was made in sufficient quantity to provide ample - nay, generous - portions for all. And, where a dish might require extensive cooking time, as, for example, a roast duck, Maurice would demonstrate up to the point of oven insertion and then produce a previously cooked duck for immediate consumption. As there was usually soup, a fish or shellfish appetizer, at least two meat and fowl entrees and at least one dessert, each with its appropriate unfamiliar wine, the cooking class was held by some to be the biggest bargain not only in the west. The tab started out at about $10, and ultimately reached about $90 with tip roughly a quarter century later, when Maurice retired from the Alps to devote himself to tennis. Some "students" were serious disciples, taking notes and mimeographing (remember that?) them for the rest. Others unabashedly came solely to eat, and went into training for several days before the gustatory orgy. Everyone learned something, even the just plain eaters. The real cooks got tips from a master on how to make masterpieces. The klutzes acquired little tricks of the trade that the real cooks already knew, like not adding water to spinach but cooking it in only the wash water, or getting a spouse to eat zucchini by sautéing in garlicky butter plus nutmeg! or keeping the kitchen spotless by washing utensils in cooking intermissions while telling jokes.

And speaking of utensils, even such unexpected places as the thrift shop played a part in Aspen's culinary life, by supplying the cooking gadgets the living quarters did not.

The most direct association of the Physics Center as a whole with food was through its picnics. The current weekly picnics on the Center's grounds were not eternally thus. Early picnics were held at a different spot each week: Difficult Campground, The Meadows near the river....And once a month, instead of a picnic, there was a cocktail party in the patio. A modest fee ($3 per couple in 1973) covered the cost of imbibements and everyone was supposed to bring a dish of something. Culinary talent not being uniformly distributed, it got to be known after a while who would be sure to appear with what. And so some physicists wouldn't fill themselves too full in anticipation of a Berry quiche or a personally caught Block trout, personally smoked and brought by another Block because the catcher doesn't eat fish. Both quiche and trout never quite made it to the food table, having been involuntarily distributed en route. A small number of people nibbled and then went out to dinner afterward. Most made the cocktail party their dinner.

As the years went by and the Center personnel changed, first with more singles - who didn't cook and would bring City Market guacamole or potato salad, so that there'd be at least five of each on the table, which the "management" tried to offset with (always the same) cold cuts - and then more young families with small children and baby sitting problems, plus the effort required of the Center Staff, the cocktail party was phased out.

Another no longer extant gustatory experience associated with the Physics Center was the trout fry at Toklat, on the Ashcroft Road. That lasted until fairly recent times. Stuart Mace would provide fresh trout, steak and a multigrain dish if about fifteen or so eaters could be rounded up. A nature talk would often accompany the repast and, in the first few years, when Mace still had the sixty-odd huskies he bred for dog sledding in the winter, before he bequeathed them to Krabloonik in Snowmass, he'd conduct visits to the dogs' quarters and, approaching his head dog, say to him to "Give us a song boys", whereupon this over-two-hundred pound obliging creature would lift his chin and croon "Aaawoooooooooooo!" followed by the entire chorus of sixty joining in on a second longer "Aaawoooooooooooo!" the musical part of the evening.

Hiking ordinarily makes people hungry, or thirsty, or both. Some Center hikers made it a point to go out to dinner after a hike with their fellow hikers of the day. In the earliest years of the Center there was another after-a-hike tradition, immediately after, before going home - a thick shake in Carl's Pharmacy! Yes, Carl's Pharmacy. Look at the sign over the door. It says: "Carl's Pharmacy, Prescriptions and Sodas". Ever wonder about the sodas? Ever see the sign? Well, years ago, on the left side of Carl's, where the magazines are now (and probably the liquor store as well) was an old fashioned soda fountain. Ice cream was not yet outlawed, and the shakes were western style, so thick you couldn't use a straw. You shouldn't use a straw on such shakes anyway, to get all taste buds on alert for maximum flavor.

Those shakes were a real treat for deprived Easterners who knew only the kind you drank, rather than ate with a spoon. They weren't even called shakes back East; they were malteds (New York) - even when they contained no malt - or (would you believe it?) phosphates (Philadelphia). Carl's called them milkshakes. Now the whole country probably has homogenized the term to shakes.

At the end of a stay there were always the leftovers to dispense. For those stays in the beginning or middle of the summer it was easy: there were always people staying another week or two to dump on. But at the end of the summer there weren't any more dumpees. Then the pepper and the cinnamon, etc. would end up in the storeroom of Stranahan Mall or with a local acquaintance. Some locals would resupply their donors the following year if they hadn't used what was dumped on them. Some tins of pepper probably have been cycled and recycled back and forth for twenty years. There may even be a record holding tin that's been moving through Aspen cupboards since the Center began.

One might pause at this point to ask at whom this cookbook is aimed since, while there have been some really good cooks associated with the Center, many of whom have contributed recipes, there are also a great many who may be lumped into the category represented by the (known) three who savored the cat food pellets in the DeWolf kitchen at a party, under the impression they were another of the interesting hors d'oevres. Nevertheless, there'll be something for everybody. So cook, eat and be merry, for tomorrow ye may diet!

*10^8 is 100 million, that is, 100,000,000.

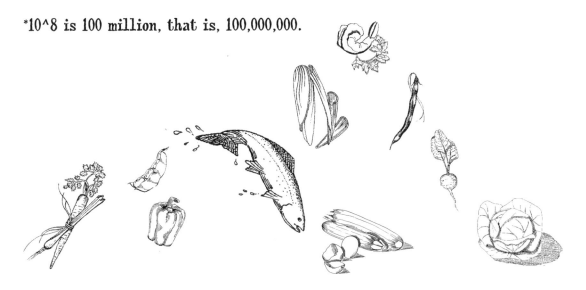

Dr. Grace Marmor Spruch is Professor of Physics at Rugers University, New Brunswick, NJ and the author of many articles for scientific journals as well as a book about life with a remarkable group of urban squirrels, "*Squirrels in the Window*", published by William Morrow & Co, Inc. She and her physicist husband Larry are long-time summer participators in workshops at the Aspen Center For Physics.

Chaos and Symmetry are pleased to present the culinary genius of five very extraordinary chefs:

Dr. Peter Carruthers
Timothy B. Durand
Dr. Chih-Hao Huang
Tita Alvarez Jensen
Dr. Harold McGee

Extraordinary Chef,
Dr. Peter Carruthers

Dr. Peter Carruthers (1935-1997), Professor of Physics at the University of Arizona, brought enthusiasm and a high degree of skill to his many interests and to his profession as a particle physicist. He was a fly fisherman and a chef, a violinist and an artist, an inveterate traveler and a man who made many friends in the far corners of the world. He first came to the Aspen Center for Physics in 1962, returning for many years thereafter. He is sorely missed by his friends and colleagues.

Trout Recipes

Small Trout - up to 8 inches

Clean well, scrub and leave heads on. Salt and pepper and coat with flour. To make more crust, first dip the trout in milk. Heat some butter (never margarine!) and olive oil until hot but not burning. I prefer a thick aluminum pan for this purpose, brown both sides until crisp and serve with lemon and watercress.

Medium Trout - 8 - 14 inches

This is an awkward size to sauté. A good way to keep them moist is to wrap in foil (with a few slits for overpressure, and then to lay them on a not too hot charcoal grill). Turn at least once. Spice as you like. Try a little paprika or New Mexico hot chile. Some people like a little bacon for extra flavor.

Big Trout - say 14 -20 inches in Aspen

Clean well. Place over foil, stuff belly with cooked wild rice preferably enhanced with Steinpilze or Chanterelle or other wild mushrooms. Salt and pepper. Slit foil after wrapping and bake at 350° Fahrenheit.

All-Purpose-Poached Trout

Get a container of appropriate shape and size. Put trout in and cover with chicken broth (preferably home made) and dry white wine. Add scallions or leeks, salt and other spices to taste. Cover and simmer until done. They are done when the eyes pop out. Nice sauces can be invented to go with the trout, which I often prefer cold. Easy sauces are mayonnaise mixed with catchup or sour cream with dill and lemon juice.

Smoked Trout

Buy a smoker from a regular supplier. Be careful which wood you choose. Mesquite is good.

Extraordinary Chef, Timothy B. Durand

Executive Chef, Timothy B. Durand, who provides excellent dining at the Aspen Glen Club Restaurant in Carbondale, Colorado has an Aspen connection going back 27 years. His father, Dr. Loyal (Randy) Durand has been a member of the Aspen Center for Physics since 1962 and continues his attendance today as an honorary member.

Providing interesting dishes for a varied group of diners is Tim's specialty and he oversees a kitchen that cooks three meals a day, seven days a week. After apprenticing in Los Angeles and attending the Epicurean Cooking School there, he decided that a small town would be more to his liking and a relief from the demands of a large city. He moved to Aspen and accepted the position of chef at the Little Nell's Restaurant, moving on to Executive Chef at Sage Restaurant, Snowmass Lodge and Club and then on to several other fine restaurants in Aspen, before accepting his present position at the Aspen Glen Club.

Chaos and Symmetry are pleased to present some of Tim's recipes.

Professional Experience:

- Executive Chef, The Aspen Glen Restaurant, February 1999 - Present.
- The Little Nell Hotel, June 1998 - February 1999.
- Executive Chef of Sage Restaurant, Snowmass Lodge and Club, Snowmass, Colorado, a 4-star hotel and restaurant, August 1995 - June 1998.
- Executive Sous Chef, The Little Nell Hotel, Aspen, Colorado, April 1994 - August 1995. Assistant to renowned chef George Mahaffey at Aspen's only 5-star hotel.
- Sous Chef, The Motherlode, a fine Italian restaurant in Aspen, Colorado, April 1993 - April 1994.
- Executive Chef, The Grill on the Park, Aspen, Colorado, October 1991 - April 1993.
- Head Chef, Grill Concepts, Inc. Southern California, September 1988 - September 1991. Opened and operated three new Daily Grill restaurants in Brentwood, West Hollywood and Newport Beach, CA.
- Earlier, the noted Border Grill and at Joe Allen's in Los Angeles, CA.

Education:

- Epicurean Cooking School, 1985
- Professional Chef Training

Grilled Lamb with Chimichurry Marinade

Serves 4

INGREDIENTS

4 lamb chops, 1-inch thick

__Marinade__:

*1/2 cup parsley, cleaned, stemmed
 and chopped
2 T garlic, chopped
2 T dried oregano
1/2 cup olive oil (or more)
salt & pepper to taste*

Combine all marinade ingredients in small bowl. Coat lamb chops with marinade and grill to desired doneness.

Serving Suggestion: Serve with grilled seasonal vegetables (carrots, squash, zucchini) and sweet potatoes mashed with heavy cream and cinnamon.

Farfalla with Chicken

Serves 4

INGREDIENTS

4 skinless, boneless chicken breasts,
  cubed
2 T olive oil
1 lb farfalla pasta (cooked al dente and
  kept warm)

1/2 cup porcini mushrooms, sliced
1 cup parmesan cream sauce (see
  recipe below)
1/2 cup scallions, chopped
1/2 cup tomatoes, chopped
grated parmesan

1. In a hot pan, sear the chicken in oil. When chicken is almost done, add mushrooms, scallions (reserve some for garnish), pasta and Parmesan sauce to taste.

2. Continue cooking until chicken is cooked through. Serve immediately, garnished with scallions, chopped tomato and grated Parmesan.

Parmesan Cream Sauce

INGREDIENTS

1/2 cup onions, diced
2 large cloves garlic, chopped
1 qt chicken stock
1-1/2 qts heavy cream
2 cups parmesan, grated
salt & white pepper to taste

laurel leaf and basil sachet (wrap 3
  laurel leaves and 1/2 cup basil leaves
  in a square of cheesecloth and tie
  with kitchen string)
cornstarch
white wine

1. Sauté onion and garlic in olive oil. Add the sachet, chicken stock and heavy cream. Simmer 30 minutes.

2. Mix a little cornstarch with white wine to form a loose paste. Slowly add to cream mixture and stir until sauce thickens.

3. Remove sachet. Add parmesan, blend and strain.

4. Season with salt and white pepper.

Spinach Salad
with Bacon Vinaigrette

Serves 4

INGREDIENTS

8 oz spinach leaves, stems removed
8 oz goat cheese, crumbled
8 oz red and yellow teardrop
  tomatoes, halved

4 oz scallions, chopped
4 oz bacon, cooked and diced
4 T pine nuts, toasted

Combine ingredients and toss with bacon vinaigrette.

Bacon Vinaigrette

INGREDIENTS

1/4 cup bacon, diced
1/4 cup onion, finely diced
1/4 cup chicken stock
1/2 cup ketchup

1/4 cup pure olive oil
2 T cider vinegar
1/2 T black pepper
4 T sugar

1. Sauté bacon until one-half way done, add onions and cook until bacon is done. Drain excess grease.

2. Add remaining ingredients and heat.

3. Place ingredients in a blender and blend until emulsified. Strain.

4. Adjust seasoning and toss with spinach salad.

Extraordinary Chef, Dr. Chih-Hao Huang

Dr. Chih-Hao Huang, who has generously allowed us to include his recipes, is presently working on the Sloan Digital Sky Survey at Fermilab in Batavia, Illinois. This Survey is the most ambitious astronomical project ever undertaken and will map in detail one-quarter of the entire sky. Chih-Hao was born in Taiwan and spent his school years there until graduate school when he came to the US to attend Northwestern University in Evanston, Illinois. He received his PhD in computer science.

He says that he did not invent all the recipes he has on his website, but recalled some from his father, some from friends and a few as a result of 'reverse engineering' after eating at restaurants whose meals could use some improving. He feels that most of his recipes are easy to prepare because he has had the fun of working through each one and that even "lazy graduate students could make them."

Chaos and Symmetry are very pleased to present the recipes of Dr. Chih-Hao Huang.

Aged Dou-Fu

This is another reverse engineering on a Japanese appetizer.

INGREDIENTS

soft dou-fu
cornstarch
cooking oil
1 shredded turnip

teriyaki sauce (if you do not have
    teriyaki sauce on hand, you may use
    soy sauce with sugar and ginger
    juice)

1. Cut dou-fu into smaller chunks of 1" x 1" x 1/2".

2. In deep frying pan, heat up cooking oil that is enough to cover at least half of the dou-fu chunks when they are in.

3. Dip dou-fu chunks in cornstarch, one by one, and fry them in hot oil. Since the heat has to be maintained, do not put too many chunks in at one time.

4. Turn them a few times so that each is fried evenly on every side. Keep frying until the color turns to brown.

5. When serving, dip them with teriyaki sauce and put the shredded turnip on top.

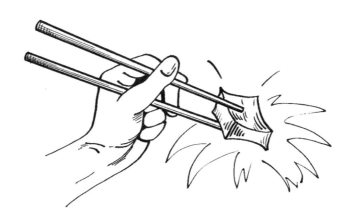

Almond Dou-Fu

Almond Dou-fu is a tasty and popular dessert.
This recipe is a kind of failure-proof recipe.
If you still mess it up, you are really something.

INGREDIENTS

*1 box almond tofu mix (you can get
  it from Chinese grocery stores)
mixed fruits or cocktail fruits (they
  come in cans of fruit chunks;
  of course you can cut the fruit
  yourself, but remember to put in
  some with beautiful colors,
  such as cherries)*

*palm seeds in syrup (palm seeds look
  translucent and have a very
  distinctive and firm texture; this is
  your secret weapon to make some
  almond dou-fu that is different
  from what your friends make)*

1. Follow the instructions on the box to make almond dou-fu. Basically, you mix it with a certain amount of water, boil it (stir frequently) and let it cool.

2. Cut the firm almond dou-fu into small chunks and mix them with the mixed fruits and palm seeds. The syrup should make it sweet enough. If not, add some sugar.

3. Keep it cool until serving. Add some crushed ice if necessary.

Hints: You do not have to use the almond dou-fu mix if it is hard to get. You may get pure jell mix and almond extract from any store. Boil the jell mix as instructed and put in a few drops of the almond extract. The extract is highly concentrated so a few drops are enough. You may start with little. If the taste is not enough, put in a couple more drops.

If you do not use jell mix, you may also use sugar and gelatin and really do it from scratch (you get more sense of achievement, too).

In all cases, if the cool almond dou-fu is not firm enough, don't worry. You can heat it up and put in more almond dou-fu mix (or jell mix, or agar), See? You can hardly mess it up!

BBQ

It's summer! It's time for BBQ.
You can do it in the park, on the lake front, or just on your back porch.

INGREDIENTS

beef, pork, or
   chicken legs
soy sauce
ginger juice
garlic juice

green onion
1 can or bottle dark beer
sugar
onion
pineapple

mushroom
green pepper
red pepper

Preparing the meat:

1. Beef: (Shishkebob) 2 lbs
   a. Use round roast (best for price and performance). Rump portion is also good.
   b. Cut into 1" cubes.
   c. Marinate with soy sauce, ginger juice, garlic juice, green onion, dark beer (the secret flavor!) and sugar. Overnight is more than enough.
   d. Make shishkebob with onion, mushroom, pineapple, green pepper and red pepper (for color).

2. Pork:
   a. Use 4-6 pork chops. On average, a person may consume 1/4 pound.
   b Smash the chops completely. This is very important for chops.
   c. Marinate with soy sauce, ginger juice, garlic juice, green onion, dark beer and sugar. Again, overnight is more than enough.
   d. Garlic is important to pork as ginger is to beef.
   e. German dark beer from Berggoff does a good job and is quite a Chicago tradition. (This is not an endorsement, though.)

3. Chicken Legs:
   a. Chicken legs may be treated the same as above.
   b. The legs must be cut open, lengthwise along the bone. Otherwise, the meat may be too thick for BBQ.

Tricks in BBQ:

   a. Lighting the grill; When most of the charcoal turns light gray and the smoke is down, the temperature is about right.
   b. ALWAYS cover the grill up! The flavor will be kept and you won't have an open flame that might burn the meat and leave the inside raw.
   c. When open flame is out of control, just cover the grill up, oxygen deprivation!
   d. Apply the marinade to the meat on the grill from time to time.
   e. Apply the BBQ sauce ONLY at the last moment before the meat is done.
   f. How do you know when a thick piece of meat (like a chicken leg) is done? It is done when you can easily separate the meat from the bone.
   g. To add a Chinese touch, you may put honey into the BBQ sauce.

Other ingredients you may consider:

   a. Taiwanese sausage: lots of pork fat, excellent for the grill.
   b. Squid: doesn't need to be marinated. Brush it with BBQ sauce on the grill.
   c. Shrimp: use larger ones. Marinated with wine or beer for only an hour, then brush it with BBQ sauce at the end.

Bean Curd and Crab Meat Soup

Running out of ideas for soup? This is another easy one.
If the ingredients are ready, you should be able to finish it in 5 minutes.

INGREDIENTS

*1 lb soft bean curd, cut into bite size
    chunks*
*1 lb crab meat, either fresh, canned or
    imitation*
2 eggs, well beaten

*2 t cornstarch, dissolved in
    water*
1 green onion, chopped
salt and pepper

1. In a stock pot, boil 2 quarts of water.

2. Put in bean curd chunks and crab meat. Wait for the water to boil again.

3. Add salt to taste.

4. Add cornstarch and stir quickly. The soup should become thicker.

5. Pour in beaten eggs, turn off heat and stir slowly to create the egg flakes.

6. When serving, sprinkle with green onion pieces and pepper.

Sweet Bean Curd Flake

Miss the sweet bean curd flake in your hometown? (especially if you came from the southeastern provinces) Though this is not a true recipe to make bean curd flake from scratch, it is a quick and simple way to satisfy your taste buds. In general, it is just bean curd flakes in peanut soup. Therefore, it is a matter of where to find the resources.

INGREDIENTS

*sweet bean curd: you may find it in Chinese
    grocery stores; if it cannot be found,
    Japanese style tofu may be used*

*sweet peanut soup, precooked and
    canned*

1. Use a flat spoon or scoop to flake the sweet bean curd. If you are using the Japanese style tofu, you may want the flakes to be thin.

2. Add sweet peanut soup to it. Isn't that easy?

Note: You can also make peanut soup from scratch. Put peeled peanuts in warm water overnight, then slow cook for hours until the peanuts become soft. This takes 1 hour if you use a pressure cooker. Add sugar to your taste. If you are using Japanese style tofu, you may want to add more sugar.

Beef Stew

Beef stew is good for a dish or for the lunch box and for beef stew with noodles. You may spend some time to make a pot and use it all week.

INGREDIENTS

1 lb beef with a little fat
stew vegetables, frozen or fresh,
*   roughly the same amount as the beef*
*   (usually carrot, onion and potato)*
star anise

soy sauce, 1/3 bowl per lb of beef
1 T sugar
a few hot peppers
ginger slices

1. Cut the beef into bite size pieces.

2. Boil the beef for a few minutes with the ginger slices to remove the odor.

3. In a fresh pot, put the anise, soy sauce, sugar and hot peppers in with water. The water should be enough to cover everything. Heat to a boil. Remember, since most of the water will be boiled out at the end, the "absolute" amount of soy sauce will determine the saltiness, not the initial ratio. You may experiment to your taste.

4. Continue to boil for a few minutes until the level drops noticeably. Add the beef, cover and allow to boil again. Turn down the heat just enough to keep it boiling.

5. Simmer for 1 hour, then add the vegetables. Simmer for another 20 minutes and

Beef Stew in Clear Soup

We have introduced several ways of stewing meat. This is another one that has no soy sauce in it. It could be a soup dish, or a soup base for noodles.

INGREDIENTS

2 lbs brisket
1 star anise
ginger slices

salt
cooking wine
cooking oil

1. Cut the beef into bite size pieces.

2. Heat up about 4 tablespoons of cooking oil in a wok, stir fry the beef chunks until the color turns and the remaining blood comes out of the beef. It might take a few minutes.

3. In a stock pot, heat up 4 quarts of water. When it boils, add beef chunks, ginger slices and star anise.

4. Allow the water to boil again and turn the heat to medium. Cover and simmer for 1-2 hours or until the beef is very tender. Add salt to taste.

5. One minute before you turn off the heat, add a few drops of cooking wine.

Broiled Fish

This recipe is a combination of reverse engineering and experiment.
Try it and you might invent your own.

INGREDIENTS

fish filet or steak; salmon, tuna, cod
   or sword fish
miso paste
sugar

cooking wine
ginger juice
honey

1. Marinate the fish with the miso paste, sugar, cooking wine and ginger juice overnight. You may experiment with the ratio. Just remember, the miso paste is the base and the others are the added flavor.

2. Wrap the marinated fish filet in aluminum foil. Heat it in a 350° Fahrenheit oven for 10 minutes or until it is done. The foil will keep the moisture and flavor in.

3. Open the foil and heat it at 500° Fahrenheit for 2 minutes or until the surface is a little bit burned.

4. Brush some honey on top and it is ready to serve.

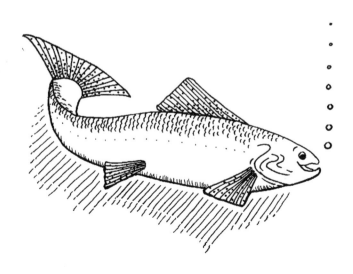

Buffalo Wings

Every one knows that buffaloes don't have wings. The famous Buffalo wings are deep-fried chicken wings topped with special hot sauce, originating from the Anchor Bar in Buffalo, New York. This recipe was reverse engineered from the wings at Buffalo Joe's in Evanston, Illinois.
The owner will never reveal the recipe to his sauce, but this is close.

INGREDIENTS

chicken wings
chicken wing sauce, preferably from
   southern Louisiana

cooking oil, peanut or corn

1. Clean up the chicken wings and let them dry. They have to be very dry to be fried crisp. You may need towels to dry them up.

2. In a deep frying pot, heat the oil to over 400° Fahrenheit. The amount of oil should be able to cover the wings and still keep the temperature. If you are using an electric fryer, set the temperature to 425° Fahrenheit.

3. Deep fry the wings for 10-15 minutes or until they are crisp. The key to a good fry is the temperature. Therefore, don't fry too many at a time because the cold wings bring down the temperature. If the temperature is too low (lower than 325° Fahrenheit), the wings will be soaked rather than crisp.

4. When the wings are done, toss them in the sauce.

You may try making the sauce as follows:
Blend hot sauce (must be from southern Louisiana) with margarine. The ratio is 1:1 for medium hot. You can adjust this to suit your taste.

Usually Buffalo wings are served with celery sticks and ranch or blue cheese dressing. That is, cut the celery into small sticks, immerse the sticks in icy water for at least 30 minutes, then dip them with the dressing.

Warning: Eating Buffalo wings is addictive.

Cabbage

Cabbage is one of the cheapest vegetables here.
Cooking cabbage is not difficult, especially with this recipe.

INGREDIENTS

2 lb cabbage
1 lb shrimp, dried or fresh, canned or
   frozen

Chinese mushrooms-woodears
salt
sugar

1. Restore the mushrooms and shrimp in warm water.

2. Cut mushrooms into small strips.

3. Cut the cabbage through the same axis, in the same way you cut oranges. Place in a bowl and add salt and sugar from the top, and a cup of water.

4. Add a cup of water to a rice cooker and put the bowl, with everything in it, into the cooker. Cover it up and steam until done.

Cantonese BBQ

This is another of Canton's very own.
Here, several ways are introduced to make it,
starting from the author's favorite one all the way to a very lazy version.

INGREDIENTS

Pork
* Chinese BBQ seasoning mix
honey

Marinade:
   cooking wine
   soy sauce
   sugar
   ginger
   green onion

1. Clean the pork and cut it into 2" x 2", however long you want (the longest dimension is along the texture of the meat).

2. Put some sugar into the soy sauce, about 1 teaspoon to 1 cup ratio, as well as some cooking wine. Sugar, one of the most powerful secret weapons in Cantonese cooking, plays an important role in the flavor. Put in a few slices of ginger and some green onion to remove the odor.

(continued on next page)

3. Marinate the pork. The pork should be fully immersed in it. A convenient and economical way to marinate meat is to put it into a food grade plastic bag, especially one with a zip lock. Squeeze out the excessive air and seal it off. The meat stays fully immersed in the marinade. Because the bag is flat you may stack several of them in the refrigerator. Marinate overnight to get the flavor into the meat.

4. Make fresh marinade and leave the pork in this for another night. When the pork is ready, preheat the oven to 400° Fahrenheit. Put the pork in the oven, making sure it is well supported by a grill and that the grease is well drained away. Cook for 30-40 minutes, checking frequently. If the surface looks too dry, dip it in the marinade and put back in the oven. Turn the meat a few times to make sure it is evenly heated.

5. In the meantime, prepare the honey. If the honey is too thick, you may dilute it with a few drops of water (not too much).

6. After 30 minutes, if the surface of the pork, especially the edges, starts to burn, it is about ready.

7. Dip the pork in the honey for the final process. The honey coating makes it easy to "burn" and gives it a smoky flavor.

8. Put the pork back in the oven and and turn the heat to the maximum. Leave it in for 3-5 minutes. About 1/4 of the surface will be burned. This is normal, however, don't let it get overcooked. When the surface is a little bit burned, turn off the heat and let it sit in the oven for another 20 minutes. If you like, you may dip the meat in the honey again.

Note:

When serving, slice the pork. The cross section should not follow the direction of the texture of the pork.

In summer, you may BBQ over open flames. You may also experiment with different ways of broiling it. For example, with stronger heat and less cooking time the pork will be tender inside. Or, try lower heat, say 300° Fahrenheit, in the first 30 minutes and the high heat in the end. It will give you better control not to burn as much.

* Cantonese BBQ mix has food colors. If you don't like this, you may use seafood paste, catsup, some cooking wine and sugar to make it from scratch. This is just an approximation, the flavor is close but not quite the same. Or, use this approximation with a little seasoning mix to gain the flavor.

Cantonese Pickled Vegetables

Cantonese Pickled Vegetables are good for an appetizer as well as a good roast duck. Best of all, it's an easy dish to make.

INGREDIENTS

6 white turnips
6 carrots
6 cucumbers without the seeds
white vinegar

sugar
<u>dry</u> jar or container that can be sealed
  (you can seal it with plastic wrap
  and a rubber band)

1. Clean the vegetables. Cut them into cubes of 1 centimeter on each side.

2. Let the vegetable cubes dry. This is very important when making pickled vegetables. Let them sit in a well drained container until there are no visible water spots on them. When dry, put them into the jar.

3. Mix the same amount of vinegar and sugar. Pour this mixture into the jar. The level should be over all the vegetable cubes. Seal the jar and let it sit in the refrigerator for 2 or 3 nights.

When serving, remember that whatever equipment you use to pick them up with must be very dry. The remaining juice is good enough for another jar of vegetable cubes. You can use the same juice over and over, just add a little more vinegar/sugar mix when necessary.

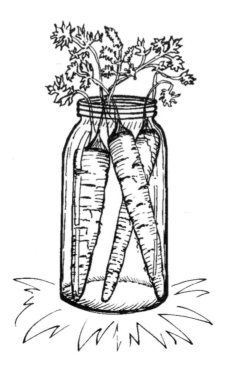

Chinese Bun

In the USA, there are many convenient foods for busy people. One of these is half-made biscuits that are cooked by throwing them (not literally) in the oven for a few minutes. Such biscuit dough rises and may be used as a wrapper for Chinese buns if they are steamed and not baked.

INGREDIENTS

4 oz ground pork
cabbage leaves
ginger

1 t sugar
1 t salt
1 container ready-made biscuit dough

1. Chop the cabbage and ginger.

2. Mix the chopped cabbage, ginger and ground pork with salt and sugar. This is the filling.

3. Wrap the filling in the biscuit dough. Just think about what a bun looks like and wrap it like that. Twist the top firmly so the filling is tightly wrapped inside.

4. Steam the buns until they are done. For 8 buns in a rice steamer, 1 cup of water will be enough. If you steam them in a conventional wok, it might take 5-10 minutes. You may want to place a few cabbage leaves underneath the buns so they won't stick to the plate.

Variations: You may try different ingredients in the filling, such as Chinese mushrooms, dry shrimp, sour bamboo shoots, etc.

Chicken Stew

Chinese style stew means stew with soy sauce and some spices, especially star anise.
Usually, you stew the meat with some vegetables.
Chicken stew is just one of the examples.

INGREDIENTS

2 lbs chicken meat
1 can bamboo shoots, whole or in
* halves*
star anise

soy sauce
sugar
corn starch
cooking oil

1. Cut the chicken into small pieces.

2. If necessary, cut the bamboo shoots.

3. Marinate the chicken with soy sauce, a little bit of sugar and a little bit of corn starch. Make sure every piece is well covered and leave for 20 minutes.

4. In a hot frying pan with a cup of cooking oil, pan fry the chicken until the surface turns brown.

5. In a stock pot, combine the chicken pieces and bamboo shoots, 1 cup of soy sauce, a few star anise, 2 teaspoons sugar and water. The water should cover everything in the pot. If you like, you may add a few hot peppers.

6. Heat the mixture to boiling and keep it boiling with minimal heat for another 30 minutes.

7. Turn the heat to high and boil until the liquid in the pot is evaporated to 1/3 its original amount, the turn off the heat completely.

Variations:
You may use other vegetables, such as carrots or potatoes.
You may also use other meat, such as small pork ribs.

Corn and Ground Pork

What is the crop that the state of Illinois produces the most? Corn!
Here is an easy recipe to have corn the Chinese way.

INGREDIENTS

4 oz ground pork
1 lb cut corn

__Marinade__:
> *spoonful soy sauce*
> *sugar*
> *few drops cooking wine*
> *cornstarch*
> *crushed garlic*
> *cooking oil*
> *dark vinegar*

1. Blend the marinade ingredients well, according to taste, and let the pork sit in it for 10 minutes.

2. Heat a stir fry pan with the cooking oil in it. When the oil is hot, add the crushed garlic. When the garlic turns a little bit (not too much) brown, put the marinated pork in the pan and stir fry quickly.

3. When the color of the pork turn from pink to brown, add the cut corn and continue to stir fry for about 2 minutes.

4. At this point, taste it and see if it is salty enough. If not, add a little more salt. If it is too salty, add more corn.

5. Finally, add a little dark vinegar, stir fry, and turn off the heat. It is ready to serve.

Hint: You may add a little red pepper with the corn for color.

   If you like, you may heat the corn in the microwave. Cut it, heat at full power for about 4 minutes, and add butter and salt.

Variations: Use ground beef instead of pork, sweet green peas instead of corn (delete the vinegar in this case), or corn, peas and red pepper together. Adding chopped onion will increase the flavor.

Curry Chicken

Curry chicken is a good dish for the lunch box and is something
you can make during the weekend and consume during the week.

INGREDIENTS

1/2 chicken (about 2 lbs) or 4 legs
   (pork or beef can be used)
1-2 potatoes (peeled)
1/2-1 lb carrots
1 onion

curry paste (not red curry)
cooking oil
green onion
hot pepper (optional)

1. Cut chicken, potato (peeled), carrots and onion into bite sized chunks. Cut the
green onion into small pieces.

2. Heat the wok with 1/2 cup cooking oil. Put in cut green onion, let it fry for 30
seconds, add onion chunks and fry for 1 minute, then add chicken chunks and fry
for a few minutes until it turns color. Add potato and carrot and stir fry for a
minute or two.

3. Put in 2 quarts of water and curry paste. When it boils, blend well and turn the
heat to medium. Cover and let simmer for 45-60 minutes, blending from time to
time to prevent the bottom from burning. Add more salt or curry paste according
to taste. Serve over steamed rice.

Dou-fu Skin Roll

Dou-fu skin rolls are a nice appetizer.
It is good for treating yourself as well as impressing your guests.

INGREDIENTS

canned, shredded bamboo shoots   *star anise*
Chinese mushrooms, fresh or dried   *sugar*
fresh (quick frozen) dou-fu skin   *cooking wine*
soy sauce   *sliced ginger*

1. If the mushrooms are dried, use warm water to restore them. When this is done, wash them several times. If they are not shredded, slice them into strips.

2. Make the rolls with the mushrooms and bamboo strips. Put these vertically on one side of the skin, leaving half of the length of the vegetables vacant on each side. Fold this vacant area horizontally over the vegetables, covering them completely, and roll all the way through. Use food quality thin rope to tie up the roll. You may need 2 ties 1/3 of the length toward each end.

3. Assuming you have 8 rolls, in a 6 quart pot, pour half a bowl of soy sauce, a slice of yellow sugar block or ordinary sugar, a few slices of ginger, a little cooking wine, star anise and 2-3 quarts of water. You may add a few hot peppers if you like. Heat to boiling.

4. Put the rolls in the pot. When it returns to a boil, turn down the heat just enough to keep it boiling. Let it boil for 10 minutes and turn off the heat. Allow the rolls to sit in the pot.

5. Serve the rolls cold, sliced like you slice sausages. Add some coriander on the top.

Dry-Cooked String Beans

Ever wonder what to do with string beans when they are in season.
Why not try making dry-cooked string beans, a dish with a well known name.

INGREDIENTS

1 lb string beans
4 oz ground pork
soy sauce
sugar

salt
cooking oil
chopped garlic
corn starch

1. Clean the string beans and cut off both ends.

2. Marinate the pork with 1 teaspoon soy sauce, some sugar and some corn starch for 10 minutes.

3. Heat 1 cup of cooking oil in a frying pan, add chopped garlic and stir fry for 30 seconds. Add string beans and fry for 5 minutes, stirring occasionally.

4. Add a teaspoon of sugar and continue to stir fry until the beans show signs of being burned. (The sugar is to speed up the burning process.)

5. Add salt as needed. Put in ground pork and continue to stir fry until done. Before serving, drain off the excessive cooking oil.

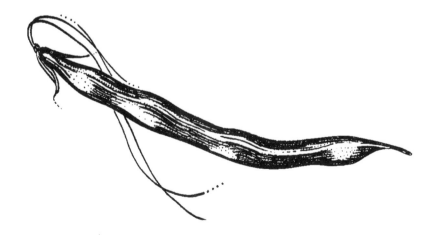

Egg Drop Soup

Egg drop soup is a really easy one

INGREDIENTS

salt

water

ginger

flavor (chicken, neck bone, pork slice,
   or beef slice or chicken or beef cube)

canned soup (cream of chicken or
   chicken broth)

beaten egg

green onion

pepper

1. First, make the soup base. Stew the flavor ingredients with a couple ginger slices for a few hours. Use minimal heat to just keep it boiling. Add salt to taste. Or, if you do not want to spend time making it this way, you may use the beef or chicken cubes. One cube is good for 2-3 quarts of soup. Just dissolve the cube in boiling water and add salt to taste. Canned soups can also be used. One 8-12 ounce can is good for at least 2 quarts of soup. You can also use boiled salty water, although this is rather tasteless.

2. While the soup base is on the stove, you may prepare the egg. One egg is good for 2 quarts of soup. Beat the egg in a bowl until well mixed.

3. Finally, you make the egg drops. TURN OFF the heat first, then pour the beaten egg into the soup. Use a pair of chopsticks to stir the soup while adding the egg. The speed of the stirring will determine the size of the egg drops. Faster stirring makes smaller drops, slower stirring makes larger drops. When serving, put some cut green onion and pepper on the top.

Variations: Use creamy corn or cream of chicken soup as the base, add some cut corn kernels and chicken meat or ham.

Using leftover soup base, you can add bean sprouts for bean sprout soup, or water cress for water cress soup. There are many other possibilities.

Five Spice Tea-Leaf Eggs

Remember the delicious tea-leaf eggs from your hometown?
It is not difficult to recreate the taste using readily available ingredients.

INGREDIENTS

eggs, as many as you like
tea (you might want to use strong
* flavors like black or wu-long tea)*

five spice powder
soy sauce, 1 rice bowl for 12 eggs

1. Boil the eggs for 8-10 minutes or until they are firm inside. You may leave the eggs in the pot for a while after the heat is turned off.

2. When the eggs are cool, crack their shells without peeling them off. You may roll the eggs on the table to create the cracks. The cracks allow the flavor to come into the eggs.

3. Boil the cracked eggs with the tea leaves or bags (about 1 bag for 3-4 eggs), soy sauce and five spice powder. Assuming that you are making a dozen eggs, use 2/3 to 1 bowl of soy sauce and 2-4 teaspoons of five spice powder, according to your taste. Keep this boiling for 30-40 minutes.

4. After turning off the heat, let the eggs sit to soak up the flavor.

Fried Smelt

Has your mother ever told you that eating fish makes you smarter?
Fried smelt is easy to cook and is also good for the lunch box.

INGREDIENTS

1 or more smelt   cooking oil
salt

1. Clean the fish and cut it into 2-3 inch lengths. Apply a thin coat of salt to both sides of each piece.

2. Allow to sit for about 30 minutes to let the salt absorb. You may also put the fish into plastic food bags and store in the freezer for weeks.

3. Wash off the excessive salt and dry the fish with paper towels.

4. Heat the frying pan and add enough oil to cover the bottom of the pan. While the oil is not too hot, put in the fish pieces. Don't add too many at once. None of the fish pieces should be overlapped.

5. Turn the fish several times, frying both sides, until they are brown and crispy. This should only take a few minutes.

Tip: How to prevent the fish from sticking to the pan.
    There are several ways:
    a. hot-pan-cold-oil as described above
    b. use a piece of ginger to rub the pan first, while it is hot, before the oil
       is put in. This only works for a traditional iron wok.
    c. use a Teflon coated, non-stick frying pan.

Garlic Pork

This is an easy dish with a good name. In a situation where you have to feed a lot of people, it does not take too much time to make more.

INGREDIENTS

1 lb sliced pork   soy sauce
lots of garlic   sesame oil

1. Heat a pot of water to boiling. Put the sliced pork in the boiling water. When the water boils again and the pork slices turn to gray, remove them and let them cool.

2. Crush the garlic and cut the cloves into small pieces. Blend the soy sauce, sesame oil and cut garlic together. Soy sauce determines the saltiness, garlic and sesame oil give the flavor. The ratio is up to you.

3. Blend the sliced pork with the sauce mix. Once blended, remove the pork. You don't want the meat sitting in the sauce for too long or it may be too salty.

Grapefruit in Rum

Grapefruit has its own distinct flavor and rum has a good smell and together, the taste is sophisticatedly nice. This is a good kind of dessert that may surprise your guests, or, simply be a treat to yourself. Best of all, it is extremely easy to make.

INGREDIENTS

4 grapefruit   *cherry (optional)*
rum

1. Peel the grapefruit and slice it into thin slices. The direction is in the plane that is perpendicular to its axis so that the core is in the center of each slice.

2. Put the slices onto a glass plate, one plate for each serving. Do not overlap the slices. Keep it cool in the refrigerator using crushed ice.

3. When serving, drip some rum onto the plate. The depth is about the thickness of the slices. To make it even more beautiful, garnish with a cherry on the side.

Variations: If you do not like grapefruit, you may use orange or pineapple instead. If you do not have rum on hand, you may use fruit flavored cooler.

Greasy Sweet Rice

It's a tradition in southern provinces when a baby boy is one month old,
his family treats all relatives and friends with greasy sweet rice.
Of course, you do not need such a reason.
You will need a 10 cup rice steamer and a 12 inch stir fry pan.

INGREDIENTS

6 cups sweet rice	8 oz pork
2 oz dry Chinese mushrooms	1 cup soy sauce
4 oz dry shrimp	1 t sugar
4 oz fried red onion	1 cup cooking oil

1. Restore the Chinese mushrooms and shrimp with warm water. Cut the mushrooms and pork into small chunks. Marinate the pork with soy sauce and sugar for 20 minutes.

2. Heat the cooking oil in the stir fry pan. Stir fry the red onion, shrimp and mushrooms for 1 minute, then add the pork. Continue to stir fry until the pork is done.

3. Add the raw sweet rice and the rest of the soy sauce that was used for the marinade into the pan and continue to stir fry for 5-10 minutes.

4. Put everything into the rice steamer and add the same amount of water as if you were cooking that much rice from scratch. Let it sit in the steamer for a while (30 minutes) until every kernel of sweet rice is soaked and becomes swollen. Cook it in the rice steamer like you normally cook rice.

Variation: You can make this without using a rice steamer. Instead, you soak the rice for 2 hours and then stir fry with the other ingredients until it is done. In this way, you have to add water from time to time, little by little. That is, with medium heat, add a cup of water, stir fry for a minute, cover it up, repeat in 5 minutes. Do this until it is done. This might take 45-60 minutes. Or, you can cook the sweet rice in a steamer first and then stir fry as if you are making fried rice.

Green Pea and Shrimp

This is not difficult to make and its taste can survive after
a re-heat, which makes it good for a lunch.

INGREDIENTS

1 lb shrimp, fresh or cooked
8 oz green peas, fresh or frozen
ginger, cut into 1 mm chunks
1 egg white
salt

sugar
cooking oil
vinegar (optional)
cooking wine
cornstarch (optional)

1. If necessary, clean and peel the shrimp. Marinate them with 1 teaspoon of cooking wine and egg white for 10 minutes.

2. Heat 1/4 cup or more of cooking oil in a stir fry pan with ginger chunks. When the oil is hot, add the shrimp and stir fry quickly. Add the green peas and continue to stir fry. Put in a spoonful of sugar and a little salt, according to taste. The whole stir frying process should last about 3 minutes. Do not overcook. If you like, you may add a few drops of dark vinegar.

3. If you would like it to be thicker, you may add some cornstarch, If you do so, the cornstarch should be dissolved in cold water first and it should be poured into the pan at the last minutes before turning off the heat. You turn off the heat after the whole pan is boiling again. Stir frequently. One teaspoon of cornstarch is enough. When serving, you may find a white plate with green pea and red shrimp is very pleasing to the eyes, as well as the stomach.

Green Pepper and Pork Strips

Green pepper and pork strips stir fry is something that
you can do in 15 minutes, from preparation to finish.

INGREDIENTS

green peppers
pork
garlic
soy sauce

sugar
salt
cooking wine
cornstarch

1. Cut the pork and green peppers into small, thin strips. Marinate pork with soy sauce, a little bit of sugar, a few drops of cooking wine and some cornstarch for 5-10 minutes.

2. Crush the garlic or cut it into small chunks.

3. In a hot wok with cooking oil in it, stir fry the garlic for 30 seconds, then add the green pepper and pork strips with a little salt and continue to stir fry for 3-5 minutes, until the pork is done. Taste it from time to time to see if it needs more salt.

Variations: You may use beef instead of pork. If you do, add ginger strips instead of garlic. You may also use shredded carrots instead of green pepper strips, or red pepper to make it more colorful.

Ham and Egg

How many kinds of dishes can you make using mainly eggs?
Ham and egg is another example. After all, you could learn a lesson from it
(see the bottom of this recipe).

INGREDIENTS

sliced ham   *cooking oil*
4 eggs   *salt*
green onion

1. Cut the ham and green onion into small chunks. Beat up the eggs and add a little salt. Save aside some cut ham and onion and put the rest into the beaten egg.

2. Put just enough cooking oil in the frying pan to make a thin coat on the bottom. Heat it up, with the ham and onion, on low heat.

3. Before the pan gets hot, pour in the egg. Move the pan in a circular fashion so the egg is spread evenly over the bottom. When the bottom of the "egg cake" is firm, turn it to heat the other side. Don't overcook it, the surface should be light brown.

There is a moral lesson behind this:

What's the difference between involvement and commitment? In this case, the chicken (who gave the eggs) is involved, yet the pig (who gave the ham) is committed.

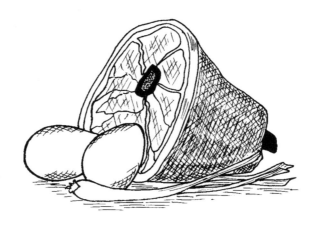

Mushroom Chicken Soup

Mushroom chicken soup is easy to make and good served cold.

INGREDIENTS

cornish hen, the little chicken with tender taste, usually sold in pairs. Ordinary chicken meat is all right

Chinese mushrooms, 10-20 pieces or so, usually sold dried and have to be restored using warm water for 10 to 20 minutes.
sliced bamboo shoots, comes in a can or jar
a few slices of ginger root

1. Clean the hens or chicken.

2. Heat 3 quarts of water in a 6 quart pot to boiling.

3. Put all ingredients into the pot, cover it, when it is boiling again, turn down the heat, just enough to keep it boiling.

4. Keep it boiling for another 30 ÷ 40 minutes.

5. Taste it, put in enough salt to flavor, then turn off the heat. You may add some cooking wine before turning the heat off.

Tip: if you are using ordinary chicken meat, you may cut it into pieces, stir fry it with cooking oil with a few slices of ginger root until the color turns, then continue with the above procedure.

Mussel Basil

This recipe is a reverse engineering from
Siam, the famous restaurant on 55th Street in New York

INGREDIENTS

1 lb mussels with shells, 1/2 lb without
4 oz basil leaves
10 dried hot peppers
cooking wine
cooking oil

salt
soy sauce
ginger slices
cornstarch dissolved in water

1. Clean the mussels.

2. Put 4 spoons of cooking oil into a stir fry pan and heat it up. When the oil is hot, stir fry the hot peppers and half of the basil leaves until the basil is a little bit burned. You should notice the distinct smell from the basil leaves.

3. Add the ginger slices, mussels and the rest of the basil leaves and stir fry for about 3 minutes.

4. Add a cup of water, some cooking wine, salt and soy sauce. Simmer for a few minutes until it is about half dry. Taste and add more flavorings as desired.

5. Add dissolved cornstarch and, when it is boiling again, turn off the heat. Garnish with lemon slices, red pepper and/or basil leaves.

Tips: You can get live mussels from the fish markets or frozen mussels from the seafood section in the grocery store. If you get live ones, remember never to throw live mussels in the refrigerator directly because it would take days for them to die, after exhausting all their protein. That is, there is not much left after. They may live for several days in clean water. Cook them while they are alive. If the mussels have shells on, they might hurt the Teflon coating of non-stick pots.

Mustard Celery

Mustard celery is a cold dish best served with greasy food,
such as roasted duck and roasted turkey. This recipe is also a reverse engineering.

INGREDIENTS

celery

honey dijon mustard

sugar

salt

vinegar

1. Clean the celery, remove the skin if it is too hard and cut it into sticks of your finger size. Or, you may use ready-cut celery.

2. Boil the celery for 1-2 minutes.

3. Blend the celery sticks with some salt and sugar and let sit for a few hours in the refrigerator. Don't use too much salt because celery is rich in sodium.

4. When serving, blend honey dijon mustard with some wine and vinegar. Taste the mixture and see if you like the flavor. You may adjust the ratio according to your taste. Then blend this mixture with the celery.

Pastry (With a Chinese Touch)

You may find lots of convenient pastry materials, such as biscuits and crescents, in the grocery stores. They are good enough as is. However, you may add a Chinese touch that will certainly impress your friends.
Or, you may just treat yourself without any special reason, right?

INGREDIENTS

crescent dough;
   comes in package of 4-8

dried pork

butter

1. Wrap the dried pork in each of the crescent doughs.

2. Cover a baking pan with aluminum foil and spread a thin layer of butter on the surface. Put the crescent dough on the pan, leaving some space in between.

3. Bake at 400° Fahrenheit for 8 minutes. The actual temperature and time may vary. Check the instructions on the package for best results. Once they are done, remove them from the oven immediately.

Pickles and Ground Pork

Here is one more way you can fix ground pork.

INGREDIENTS

1 can pickles
1 lb ground pork
a few Chinese mushrooms

a few dried shrimp
1 egg white

1. Restore the mushrooms and shrimp in warm water, separately, of course.

2. Chop the mushrooms, shrimp and pickles into small pieces. Blend these with the ground pork, egg white and pickle juice and put into a shallow pan.

3. Steam the pan for 10-15 minutes. If you are using a rice steamer, 1 cup of water will be enough.

Hint: You may serve this as a dish or pour on top of white rice. If you feel the recipe is too meaty, you may add chopped water chestnuts.

Pork Chops

From time to time you may find that pork chops are on sale.
Fried pork chops are easy to cook and are good for the lunch box, too.

INGREDIENTS

pork chops (as many as you like)
sliced ginger
soy sauce and water (1:1 ratio)

1 t cooking wine and
1 t sugar

1. Smash the pork chops using a meat hammer or the back of a chopping knife. They should be thinner after this. The purpose is to destroy the texture of the meat so that it is tender.

2. Marinate the pork with the ginger, the soy sauce/water mixture and the wine/sugar mixture. You may do this in plastic bags, overnight in the refrigerator.

3. Wash out the marinade before cooking. Heat a frying pan with a depth of oil about half that of the pork chops.

4. Pan fry the pork in medium heat. It might take about 3 minutes for each side. It really depends on the thickness of the chops and the temperature of the oil. Just don't overcook them. When you see the first sign of burning on the edge you know they are done. Hotter oil takes less time and makes the meat more tender.

Pork Kidney or Liver

Pork kidney and liver have been considered nutritious food in China. Traditionally, people think they are especially good for women who just gave birth.

INGREDIENTS

pork liver or kidney
cooking wine (rice wine is good)

black sesame oil
shredded ginger

1. Cleaning: consider the original use of these organs. We know that cleaning them is very important. To clean the kidney, cut each one in half and carve out the inner portion. You may further cut it into smaller pieces. For the liver, wash and slice it into thins pieces. Immerse in clean water over night (in the refrigerator, of course).

2. In a stock pot, combine cooking wine, black sesame oil and water in the ratio 1:1:2. Add shredded ginger and heat to a boil.

3. Put in the liver or kidney and turn off the heat after 30 seconds. The timing depends on the thickness of the liver slices or the size of the kidney pieces. The key is that you want to boil out the blood but not overcook. Serve immediately while it is hot.

Hint: If the kidney piece is considerably large, you may carve several grooves on the side of each piece. When they are cooked, they will be curly.

Pork Rib and Squid Stew

Ingredients with strong flavors are good in stews. Squid is one of them.
In rib and squid stew, the flavors will take care of themselves.

INGREDIENTS

2 lbs pork ribs, 1" strips   *sugar*
7 oz dry squid   *ginger slices*
soy sauce   *green onion*
cooking wine

1. Clean the ribs and cut them between the bones into small pieces. Pay close attention to the cross section of the bone while you are cleaning for bone fragments.

2. Restore the dried squid in warm water. After it is restored, clean it by peeling off the skin. If the squid is large, cut it into 2" x 1" pieces.

3. In a pot, stir fry the ribs and squid in hot cooking oil until the color turns.

4. In a stock pot, heat up 1 cup of soy sauce, 1/2 cup of sugar, a few ginger slices, some green onions and 2 quarts of water to a boil.

5. Add the ribs and squid to the pot and cover. When it boils again, turn down the heat to just enough to keep it boiling. Keep it simmering for 40 minutes.

6. Add some cooking wine, turn the heat to high, open up the cover and wait for the sauce to be reduced by half. Stir from time to time to prevent over cooking on the bottom. This should take about 5 minutes.

Variations: You may try other ingredients such as flavored dry bamboo shoots, mushrooms, etc.

Potato Salad

Potato salad is good for a dish on the table as well as for the lunch box.
It could also be the main course itself, with or without the bread.

INGREDIENTS

potatoes
pickles (1/2 the amount of potatoes)
eggs and ham (1/2 the amount of
   pickles)

raisins
mayonnaise
sugar
salt

1. Boil the eggs. When they are cool, peel them and cut them into halves. Separate the yolk and the egg white.

2. Peel and cut the potatoes and cut the pickles, cooked egg white and ham into small cubes.

3. Boil the potatoes. To do this, heat water to boiling, add potato cubes and boil again. Keep boiling for 5 minutes or until the cubes turn half transparent. They are overcooked if they turn completely transparent. Take away the potatoes immediately and drain off the excessive water. You may try boiling the whole potato (with skin) first before peeling and cutting. For peel-cut-then-boil, you save the boiling time but you have to drain it off properly. For boil-peel-then-cut, you trade the cooking time with better control.

4. Mix mayonnaise with the yolk, add a lot of sugar and a little salt.

5. Blend potato, pickle, ham, eggs and raisin together and add sugar and salt as needed.

Variations: You may use cooked sweet peas for green and/or apples or cucumbers instead of pickles.

Salty Duck

Making salty duck is easier than it appears.
It is also good for all occasions, cold or warm.

INGREDIENTS

1 whole duck, 4-5 lbs　　　　　　　　*spice*
salt　　　　　　　　　　　　　　　*cooking wine*

1. Clean the duck, removing excess fat under the skin near the end. Let it dry, then put cooking wine all over and inside the duck. Use your hands to rub the wine into the skin and meat.

2. Apply salt to the duck, inside and out, rubbing thoroughly into the skin and meat.

3. Put the duck into a clean plastic bag and let it sit in the refrigerator for 2 or 3 nights.

4. (A few days later) Prepare a large wok to boil the duck. Usually, it takes an 8 quart container for a 4-5 lb duck. If you do not have such a big wok, you may cut the duck and do it in batches. Put 4-5 quarts of water into the wok, enough to immerse the whole duck, and heat it to boiling.

5. When the water is boiling, put the duck in. You don't have to wash off the salt.

6. Wait for the water to boil again, turn the heat to medium, just enough to keep it boiling. Let it boil for 20 minutes, then turn off the heat. Let the duck sit in the soup for another 30 minutes, then remove.

Note: Another way to cook it is steaming instead of boiling. Steaming is especially good for smaller pieces, like a half or quarter of the duck, and is very convenient if you are using a rice cooker. However, if you do steam it, remember to wash the salt off first or it will be too salty.

Seaweed

Pickled seaweed goes best with greasy food, such as roasted duck.
This recipe was first learned from a legend who still lives in a Chicago suburb.

INGREDIENTS

shredded seaweed
soy sauce
dark vinegar
cooking wine

star anise
white sesame
sugar

1. Mix the soy sauce, vinegar, cooking wine and sugar in ratio of 2:1:1:1. In a large stir fry wok, mix this with the star anise and heat to boiling. Stir frequently to prevent it burning on the bottom.

2. Add the shredded seaweed and keep it boiling for 5 minutes, stirring frequently, and turn off the heat.

3. Dry roast the sesame and spread it on the seaweed when serving.

Shrimp

In the Midwest, good seafood is hard to find, especially if you want it to
be done in a Chinese way. Here is a very easy recipe that you can do at home.

INGREDIENTS

shrimp, as many as you like
    (remember, a fresh shrimp always
    has its head on)
cooking wine, enough to cover all
    the shrimp in the pot

white vinegar
ginger root

1. Clean the shrimp by getting rid of the intestine line from its back. This might be the most tedious part, but it is necessary.

2. Cut ginger root into fine chunks, smash them, and put them into a bowl of clear vinegar. This is the dip.

3. Heat the cooking wine in a pot to a boil and add the shrimp. When the color of the shrimp turns to red, it is done. Don't over cook them. The alcohol will evaporate, leaving only the flavor. When serving, dip the shrimp into the ginger-vinegar mix.

Variation: For very fresh shrimp, you may try steaming instead of boiling.

Simmered Bean Curd

If you are running out of ideas for cooking bean curd, here is another one.
Not knowing where the name came from, after being slowly simmered the holes
build up all over the bean curd. Though it doesn't look good, it tastes good.

INGREDIENTS

16 oz bean curd
2 oz ground pork
green onions, cut
3 T Cantonese seafood paste
1 T soy sauce

1 T sugar
black pepper powder
salt
flavored clear soup
hot peppers

1. Marinate the ground pork with the seafood paste, soy sauce, sugar, black pepper
powder and salt for 15 minutes.

2. Boil the bean curd for 2 minutes, dry it up and cut it into bite sized cubes.

3. Heat up 4 tablespoons of cooking oil in a stir fry wok, put in some green onion
and, if you like, a few hot peppers. Stir fry for about 30 seconds.

4. Put in the marinated pork and continue to stir fry until the color of the pork
turns brown.

5. Add the bean curd and a bowl of flavored clear soup. Stir without breaking the
bean curds.

6. Cover and turn the heat to medium. Simmer until the liquid is reduced by half
the original amount. Stir from time to time to avoid burning on the bottom. It
might take roughly 15 minutes to cook.

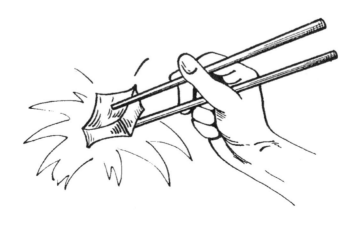

Simple Chicken Legs and Green Onion Chicken

Legs are the cheapest portion of the chicken sold in the US.
Why don't we try some simple ways to take this advantage?

INGREDIENTS

chicken leg, with thigh   *salt*
Chinese spices

Let's make spiced salt first. Use a sauce pan with medium heat. (You may control the temperature by adjusting the distance between the pan and the fire.) Put the salt and the spice into the pan in a 3:1 ratio. Don't add anything else. Basically, you are roasting the salt and spice. Stir the salt and spice frequently so they are well blended. If the pan has a handle, you may shake the pan. It takes a few (about 5) minutes, until the salt turns brown and you notice the smell.

The next step is to apply the spiced salt to the chicken. Clean the chicken, then rub the spiced salt into it all over. Having done this, put the chicken into a clean plastic bag and throw it in the freezer. It takes a few hours for the taste to get into the meat. It may stay in the freezer for weeks.

When you are ready to prepare it, remove it from the freezer and defrost it. Wash out the remaining salt. If you have a rice steamer, you may steam it in there. Put the chicken in a well drained container. Underneath, you may want to put a large bowl to catch the juices, Put one cup of water in the outer gap and steam it. This can actually be done at the same time as you cook the rice. Just make sure that a clean bowl is put under the chicken to lift it above the rice.

If you do not have a rice steamer, you may use an ordinary wok, pot or whatever container you have with a cover. Put water into the container. Put the chicken on a plate, put the plate in the container with some support, cover and steam for about 10 minutes. You may want to lift the chicken off the plate so it is not sitting in the juice. A pair of chopsticks works well for this.

A variation to this is green onion chicken. You may use other parts of the chicken. The process is the same. The additional portion is green onion and hot oil. Cut the green onion into very thin strips. Use as much as you want. Put half of them on a plate, put cut chicken on top, and put the rest of the onions on top if the chicken.

Put cooking oil into a sauce pan with some salt and heat it up. Stir it a bit to let the salt dissolve faster. It takes a few minutes to heat up the oil. Be careful, the oil is hotter than boiling water, don't hurt yourself.

Pour the hot oil over the chicken. Be very careful, when hot oil and water meet they tend to generate some noise and splash. You should notice the flavor coming out of the heated green onion.   **Enjoy!**

Snow Cabbage Pork Strip Noodles

If you don't want to spend a lot of time fixing a meal, this is another easy idea. It takes about 15-30 minutes from start to finish.

INGREDIENTS

1 can pickled cabbage　　　　　*cooking wine*
bean sprouts　　　　　　　　　*sesame oil*
2 oz pork　　　　　　　　　　*green onion*
cornstarch　　　　　　　　　　*garlic*
soy sauce　　　　　　　　　　*noodles*
sugar

1. Cut the pork into small strips. Marinate the pork strips with soy sauce, a little sugar, a few drops of cooking wine and a little cornstarch for 10 minutes. Because the cornstarch will make it sticky, you will not need much soy sauce.

2. When the pork is well marinated, you may prepare for stir frying. Start with crushed garlic in hot cooking oil, then add pork strips. Stir fry for a while and when the color turns add the cabbage and bean sprouts. Stir fry for a few minutes, then turn off the heat. This is done.

3. Put cut green onion, a teaspoon of soy sauce, a little salt and a few drops of sesame oil into a bowl.

4. Heat water to boiling, then add the mix from the previous step and raw noodles. Cook for 2-3 minutes, depending on your taste for hard or soft noodles. Remove the noodles while the water is still boiling, then turn off the heat.

5. If you already have flavored soup, you may pour it in the bowl with the noodles. If not just use the same water as soup. Pour the snow cabbage and pork strips on top of it.

Tips: It's better to have flavored soup. Don't boil the noodles in the soup directly. Boil the noodles separately and pour the soup in.

If you are really picky about the noodles, try throwing them into cold water first (10 seconds is enough) right after being taken from the boiling water. You can tell the difference.

To make sure you can finish it in 15 minutes, here is the right sequence: marinate the pork first, then boil the water and cut the green onion. You can stir fry the cabbage and boil the noodles at the same time.

If you think using canned pickled cabbage is kind of an insult to your intelligence, you can try making it from scratch.

You can get "Mustard Green" from almost any grocery store. Wash the leaves, use a well drained container with a flat bottom, then put the mustard green leaves and salt into the container as follows: one flat leaf, one layer of salt, another flat leaf, another layer of salt, etc. When this is finished put some pressure on top. What happens is the salt (in high concentration) will induce the water to come out of the leaves. This is why you need a well drained container. Leave it like this for two nights. Then completely wash out the salt and excessive water. Cut the leaves to whatever size you wish.

Soy Sauce Chicken

Soy sauce chicken is a delicious and popular Cantonese dish.
It is not an easy one. At least, it doesn't look easy.
If you do it, you certainly will impress a lot of people, including yourself, perhaps.

INGREDIENTS

fresh, lean chicken
soy sauce
water (soy sauce and water
  are in a 1:1 ratio)
1 T oyster sauce
sliced ginger

green onion
sugar, yellow or crystallized
spice
cooking wine
hot spice (optional)

1. Cut the chicken into 2 halves.

2. Put the rest of the ingredients into a wok and boil them on high.

3. Put the chicken into the wok, with the skin facing up. When the mixture boils again, turn the heat to medium to just keep it boiling. With a spoon, pour the boiling sauce over the chicken. Continue to do this until the chicken is done, about 30 minutes.

4. Let the chicken cool down before cutting it. You may still pour the sauce over the chicken from time to time to get the best flavor.

Variation: Double the amount of sauce so that the chicken can be completely immersed. Boil the sauce, put in the chicken and boil for 6-10 minutes, turning frequently. Turn off the heat and let the chicken stay in the sauce for another hour, turning it from time to time for the best flavor.

Serving: Cut the chicken into pieces as follows: be symmetric along the back and put every piece back where it belongs so that it still looks like a chicken on the serving plate. Spread green onion and sesame oil on top.

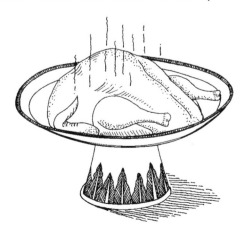

43

Spinach Stir Fry

Stir frying vegetables requires a lot of oil.
If you use animal fat, you can tell the enhanced flavor immediately.
In this environment, bacon is the best source of animal fat and flavor.

INGREDIENTS

spinach

bacon

crushed garlic

salt

cooking oil

1. Cut the bacon into short strips. According to most of the packages, the best way is to cut it across its shorter side. In such a way, each strip covers both fat and lean portions and you can cut multiple strips at once.

2. Heat the wok with some cooking oil, it does not have to be much. The purpose of the oil is to induce the fat from the bacon. Add the bacon strips and stir fry for a while. The fat should come out now.

3. Put in the crushed garlic, stir fry for 30 seconds, then add the spinach leaves. Continue stir frying for another minute or two. Add salt according to taste.

Note: This can also be done with other green vegetables, such as bean leaves.

Steamed Egg

Steamed egg, though it is not very hard, is not quite as easy as it looks.
However, if you try a few times, you should be able to get a hold of it.

INGREDIENTS

4 eggs

1 can chicken broth

1 oz ground pork

a few Chinese mushrooms

a few dried shrimp

1. Marinate the ground pork with 1/4 teaspoon salt and a few drops of soy sauce for 10 minutes.

2. Restore the shrimp and Chinese mushrooms in warm water. When they are soft, cut them into tiny chunks.

3. Beat the eggs evenly. Put them into a bowl along with the same amount chicken broth. Add the marinated ground pork and blend well. Sprinkle the cut shrimp and mushrooms on to and cover with cling wrap.

4. Steam it for 20 minutes or until done. When it is done, the eggs should look solid but still very soft. If you are using a rice steamer, 1 cup of water is enough.

Note: The secret is covering it when steaming. This is to prevent air bubbles from forming inside. The ratio of chicken broth and egg will determine the firmness. You can adjust this to suit your taste.

Steamed Pork

Steamed pork is an example of an easy cooking, nice looking and great tasting dish with a formal name. You can hardly mess it up.

INGREDIENTS

1 lb lean pork
1 sweet potato
steam powder

soy sauce
sugar
cooking wine

1. Cut the pork into small chunks.

2. Marinate the pork with the soy sauce, 1 teaspoon of sugar and a few drops of cooking wine for 20 minutes.

3. Cut the sweet potato into small chunks. Spread them on the bottom of a flat container that is to be used for steaming. The purpose of the sweet potato is to absorb the grease from the pork.   You may also use ordinary potato if you do not have sweet. Raw, frozen potato strips can also be convenient for this purpose.

4. Bread the pork chunks with the steam powder. Since the pork chunks are wet, you may simply roll them over the powder. Put these breaded chunks on top of the sweet potato, leaving some space between them. Put the container into a rice steamer with 1 cup of water. When it is done, serve immediately.

Sweet and Sour Pickles

On hot days, cold dishes are good for improving your summer appetite. Sweet and sour pickle is one of the easiest.

INGREDIENTS

pickles, as many as you like
hot pepper, optional

dark vinegar, soy sauce and sugar
mixed in a 3:2:1 ratio
sesame oil

1. Cut each pickle into 4 pieces, along its longest side.

2. In a wok, heat the sesame oil to very hot, add the cut pickle slices and hot peppers and stir fry for 1 minute.

3. Turn off the heat and pour vinegar and soy sauce in and stir a little to blend.

4. Put everything into a clean and covered container and put it into the refrigerator. It is served very cold.

Ten Vegetable Stir Fry

Ten vegetable stir fry is a very typical dish for the Chinese New Year. According to the tradition, usually the eldest person in the family will make a lot to feed the whole family for a few days. It has to be done by the new year eve.

INGREDIENTS

celery	*golden mushrooms*
bean sprouts	*bean curd strips*
carrots	*pickles*
bamboo shoots	*dried tiger lily flower*
Chinese mushrooms	*mustard green root*

1. Use warm water to restore the Chinese mushrooms and the tiger lily flower. Cut everything into thin strips. To make this easier, you may buy many of these ingredients already chopped or use a food processor.

2. Use cooking oil with high heat to stir fry the celery, bean sprout and carrot together until they are soft. Add some salt and then put them aside.

3. Reheat the wok, add a bowl of pure sesame oil, stir fry the bamboo shoots and Chinese mushrooms for 2 minutes and add the rest of the ingredients, plus the pickle juice and 2 teaspoons of sugar. Stir fry for 5-10 minutes. Add more salt and sugar according to your taste.

4. Put the celery, bean sprout and carrot back in the wok and stir fry everything together for a few minutes until they are evenly blended. You can serve this either cold or warm.

Teriyaki Mushrooms

People were wondering if there is a "short" recipe.
Here is one. It is as good as you can get from Shiroi Hana.

INGREDIENTS

mushrooms   teriyaki sauce

1. Broil the mushrooms at 350° Fahrenheit for 8 minutes or boil them for 10 minutes.

2. Top them with teriyaki sauce. Done!

Three Cup Chicken

A cup of sesame oil, a cup of cooking wine and a cup of soy sauce.
Traditionally, three cup chicken has been a nutritious dish,
especially good for women who just gave birth.

INGREDIENTS

2 lbs chicken   1 cup dark sesame oil
garlic cloves   1 cup cooking wine (rice wine is better)
sliced ginger   1 cup soy sauce

1. Cut the chicken into small chunks, 1 inch by 1/2 inch.

2. In a wok, heat a cup of the sesame oil up and add the smashed garlic and ginger slices. When the smell comes out, put the chicken chunks in and let them fry until the color turns gold.

3. Put a cup of cooking wine and a cup of soy sauce into the wok. When it is boiling, turn down the heat just enough to keep it simmering.

4. Cover it up and let it simmer for half and hour or until the liquid is 1/3 of its original quantity.

Vegetables in Oyster Sauce

Here is an easy way to make delicious vegetables in 5 minutes from beginning to end. Basically, you may apply the same recipe using any of your favorite green vegetables.

INGREDIENTS

green vegetables (mustard green,
   bokchoy, broccoli, etc.)

oyster sauce
salt

1. Boil the vegetables for 2 minutes, adding a little salt to the water to keep it green. The salt does not have to be much since the extra flavor comes from the oyster sauce.

2. Place the vegetables in a plate and drip oyster sauce on top. As you can see, if you are using a white plate, you may dress it up with all you artistic talent. A few slices of carrot on the side are a nice decoration.

Variation: If you do not use oyster sauce, you may use other dressings such as;
   1. melted cheddar cheese
   2. crab meat dressing as follows:
      boil crab meat in water and add some salt, add cornstarch dissolved in water to make it dense, add an egg white, turn off the heat and stir to make egg flakes.

Extraordinary Chef, Tita Alvarez Jensen

Tita Alvarez Jensen, a master chef, who studied under famous French chef and author, Madeleine M. Kammau at the Northeastern University in Boston, is celebrating her 20th year at the restaurant she founded: Chez Leon. Located at a crossroads where travelers from all parts of the world convene and this tiny gem of a restaurant caters to every possible palate. Physicists eat lunch at Chez Leon while discussing their theories and experiments and find it remarkably easy to evolve new ideas while being transported by Tita's delicious dishes.

Chez Leon is named for Leon Lederman, Director of the Enrico Fermi National Accelerator Laboratory from 1979 to 1989 and winner of the 1990 Nobel Prize for Physics. Tita, who was born in the Dominican Republic, had always been interested in cooking as art form and when her husband, Dr. Hans Jensen, came to the lab and stayed on as a Senior Physicist, she decided to try opening a restaurant in a small farm house using farmers' wives to help her. Since Batavia, Illinois is a long drive from Chicago, Dr. Lederman provided all the encouragement he could and today Chez Leon has a place of honor in the Users Conference Center at the National Accelerator Laboratory.

CHAOS has enjoyed many memorable occasions at Chez Leon and is pleased to include the following outstanding recipes given us by Tita.

SS. BURRUS

49

Baklava Layered Pastry

Serves 6-8

INGREDIENTS

2 cups chopped walnuts
1/3 cup sugar
1 T rose water

1 lb fillo pastry dough, thawed
1 lb butter, melted
sugar syrup

1. Combine walnuts, sugar and rose water.

2. Remove two sheets of fillo dough from package and cover remaining dough with a damp towel to prevent drying. Brush one sheet lightly with melted butter, top with second sheet and brush with more butter.

3. Spoon three to five tablespoons of walnut mixture along edge of dough. Beginning at walnut edge, roll up like a jelly roll and place in buttered 10 x 14 inch pan. Repeat with remaining dough until all of the walnut mixture is used. Lay baklava rolls close together in pan and brush the tops with butter. With a sharp knife, cut each roll diagonally into 2-3 inch lengths.

4. Bake at 300° Fahrenheit for 15-20 minutes or until golden. Remove from the oven and pour the cold sugar syrup over each piece until saturated.

Sugar Syrup

1. In a saucepan, stir together 2 cups of sugar, 1 cup of water and 2 tablespoons of fresh lemon juice. Cook over medium to high heat for 5-10 minutes or until the sugar is completely dissolved. Cool.

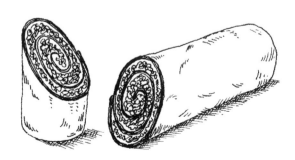

Cremè Anglaise

Serves 4

INGREDIENTS

4 egg yolks
1/4 cup sugar
1/4 t salt

1 cup milk, scalded
1 t vanilla extract

1. In a heavy saucepan, whisk together the egg yolks, sugar and salt. Very slowly add the hot milk, stirring well. With a spoon, stir continuously until the mixture has thickened and is about 165° Fahrenheit.

2. Remove the pan from heat and set in a large bowl or basin filled with ice. Whisk custard rapidly to cool it and stop the cooking process. Add vanilla and strain into a serving bowl, stirring regularly to prevent a skin from forming over the top.

Variations: For citrus flavored custard, grate 1 tablespoon of lemon, lime, orange, tangerine or grapefruit rind into the milk before making the custard. For coffee custard, add 1 1/2 teaspoons (or more) of good instant coffee to the scalded milk. For chocolate cream, mix 2 1/2 tablespoons powdered cocoa with the sugar before stirring into the egg yolk. For butterscotch cream, use dark brown sugar instead of granulated sugar.

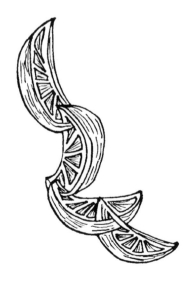

Creole Pecan Torte

Serves 6-8
INGREDIENTS

6 eggs, separated
3/4 cups sugar
1 T vanilla extract
2 cups finely ground pecans
3 T dark brown sugar

1 to 1-1/4 cups unsalted butter
1/3 cup rum
confectioner's sugar
praline powder

1. Butter and flour 3 cookie sheets. Trace a circle on each with a 9 inch pot lid.

2. Whip egg whites, adding 3 tablespoons of sugar and vanilla towards the end of the beating. Fold in 9 tablespoons of sugar and the ground pecans. Spread this on the cookie sheet circles and bake at 325° for 20-25 minutes. Cool.

3. In a blender, whip egg yolks, brown sugar and praline powder. Cream in 1 cup of butter, 1 tablespoon at a time. Add rum. If the mixture separates, add 1 or 2 more tablespoons of butter.

4. Trim the edges of the meringue layers neatly and fill with praline buttercream. Refrigerate cake for 24 hours. Sprinkle the top with confectioner's sugar before serving. Decorate the top with whole pecans.

Praline Powder

1/2 cup granulated sugar
1 t lemon juice

1/4 cup water
2/3 cup chopped pecans

1. Bring sugar and water to a boil in a heavy saucepan and cook to the hard crack stage, 310° Fahrenheit. Add lemon juice and pecans and cook 2-3 minutes longer. Pour onto a buttered cookie sheet and let cool until brittle. Break this into pieces and pulverize in a blender.

Dubonnet Pears

Serves 6

INGREDIENTS

2 cups red Dubonnet
1/2 cup orange juice
1 t grated orange rind
1-1/4 cups granulated sugar
6 ripe pears

1 lemon, halved
1 cup heavy cream
2 T Curacao
1 T minced candied orange peel
1 T sugar, or to taste

1. In a saucepan, combine Dubonnet, orange juice, grated rind and 1 1/4 cups sugar. Bring this to a boil and simmer for 5 minutes.

2. Peel the pears carefully, working with only 2 pears at a time. Rub fruit with lemon and immediately immerse in the boiling syrup. Repeat with the remaining pears. Simmer for 8-10 minutes or until tender. Chill the pears as soon as they have been poached. Reduce cooking syrup to 1 cup and cool.

3. Whip cream and add Curacao, candied peel and sugar and beat until the cream is stiff. Set 1 pear in each individual serving dish and garnish with whipped cream. Chill until serving time. When served, pass the cooled syrup.

Flan de Piña

Serves 6

INGREDIENTS

Caramel:
1 cup sugar
3 t water

Mixture:
4 eggs
2 egg yolks
14 oz condensed milk
14 oz unsweetened pineapple juice
1 t pure vanilla extract

1. To make the caramel: Combine sugar and water, melt slowly and let cook until golden brown (be careful not to burn). Take off heat and put on the bottom of 6 small soufflé dishes. After cooling, butter sides.

2. To make mixture: Whisk eggs and yolks until creamy. Add condensed milk, pineapple juice and vanilla extract. Whisk until well mixed and pour into caramelized dishes. Place in shallow pan. Fill pan with one inch of water. Place on the middle rack of a preheated 350° Fahrenheit oven for 1 hour or to the point that a knife comes out clean. To unmold, wait until cool, release with a knife around edges and invert. Serve very cold.

Note: Flan can be made with other fruit juices. 1 teaspoon of orange, lemon, or lime rind can also be used instead of the vanilla to compliment the fruit.

53

Jardiniere of Vegetables

Serves 4-6
INGREDIENTS

2 large carrots
2 large white turnips
1-1/2 cups rich, homemade veal or
   chicken stock
salt and pepper
pinch of sugar
1-1/2 T butter

1 cup green beans, cut diagonally into
   1/2 inch pieces
1 cup peas
1 head cauliflower
2/3 cup heavy cream
2 t chopped chives

1. Peel and trim the carrots and turnips and cut into 1 x 1/3 inch pieces. Round off all sharp edges with a paring knife so the vegetables can roll without breaking. In a heavy saucepan, cover with cold stock and add salt, pepper, sugar and butter. Cook until the stock has completely evaporated but has left vegetables glazed.

2. Boil green beans and peas. Drain well and add to carrots and turnips. Cut cauliflower into florets, boil and drain.

3. In a small saucepan, boil the cream until it is reduced by half. Add the chopped chives and salt and pepper to taste. Correct the seasonings of the glazed vegetables. Arrange glazed vegetables on a serving platter with cauliflower and top with reduced cream sauce.

Moro de Guandules

Serves 8

INGREDIENTS

1 16 oz can pigeon peas
2-1/2 cups long grain rice
4-1/2 cups chicken stock
1 large onion, finely chopped
4 garlic cloves, minced
1 green pepper finely chopped

1 t oregano
1 t salt
1 T cilantro, finely chopped
3 t olive oil
2 T tomato paste
1/2 t vinegar

1. Sauté onion, pepper, salt, oregano, cilantro and pigeon peas in olive oil. Add stock, tomato paste and vinegar. Bring to a boil, lower heat and add rice.

2. Uncover rice and let absorb the liquid at a slow simmer. Put heat as low as possible and cover for 20 minutes. Do not uncover during this time. Turn off heat and let rest covered for 3 minutes.

Orange Salad

Serves 6

INGREDIENTS

6 Valencia seedless oranges, peeled and
   all white membrane removed
6 green onions

12 black olives
3 T olive oil
fresh ground pepper

1. Slice oranges into 1/8 inch slices. Arrange nicely on a platter.

2. Slice scallions very thinly and sprinkle on top of oranges.

3. Arrange black olives on top.

4. Sprinkle evenly with olive oil and grind on fresh pepper.

Pescado con Salsa de Coco

Serves 6

INGREDIENTS

3 lbs red snapper filet
4 cloves garlic, mashed
2-1/2 t salt

2 limes, juice only
1-1/2 t dried oregano
1/4 t freshly ground pepper

1. Wash filets, cut two slits on the skin side. Mash all ingredients and marinate for at least two hours.

2. Pat dry, dredge in flour and fry in olive oil for about 4 minutes on each side. Serve with the following sauce.

Coconut Sauce for Fish

INGREDIENTS

1/4 cup olive oil
1 large onion, sliced very thin
4 cloves garlic, minced
1 laurel leaf
1 t dried oregano
1/4 t dried hot red pepper

1 4 oz can unsweetened coconut milk
1/2 cup chopped seeded tomato
1/2 lime, juice only
1/4 t salt
3 T fresh cilantro, for garnish

Heat oil and sauté onion, garlic, laurel leaf, oregano and pepper until golden. Add coconut milk, tomatoes, lime juice and salt. Reduce until it coats the back of a spoon. Serve with fish.

Rashida's Malaysian Coconut Shrimp Curry

Serves 6

INGREDIENTS

2 lbs shrimp, cleaned and deveined
1/2 cup peanut oil, divided
2 onions, finely chopped
2 cloves garlic, minced
1 t mustard seeds
2 laurel leaves

1 can chopped tomatoes
4 cups coconut milk
2 t coriander
1/2 t turmeric
1/2 t chili powder
1/2 t salt

1. Heat 1/4 cup oil in a Dutch oven. Sauté the onion and garlic until the onion is translucent. Add mustard seed and laurel leaves and cook for about 5 minutes. Add turmeric, coriander, chili powder, salt and 1/4 cup water. Cook, stirring for 10-15 minutes. Add tomatoes and coconut milk and simmer for 30 minutes.

2. In a large frying pan, heat remaining 1/4 cup oil and sauté shrimp until they are cooked throughout. Stir shrimp into curry sauce.

Salmon Steaks in Mushroom Butter

Serves 6

INGREDIENTS

6 salmon steaks, skinned and boned
1/2 lb mushrooms, cut julienne style
1 T lemon juice, or to taste

2 T dry vermouth
4 egg yolks
salt and pepper
1 cup unsalted butter

1. Arrange mushrooms on the bottom of a buttered baking dish. Sprinkle with lemon juice and vermouth. Arrange salmon steaks over mushrooms, sprinkle with salt and pepper and cover with buttered parchment paper. Bake at 400° Fahrenheit for 12-15 minutes.

2. Remove cooked salmon to a flameproof serving platter. Pour mushrooms and cooking juices into a small saucepan and add more lemon juice, salt and pepper to taste. Reduce liquid to 1/2 cup.

3. In a small bowl, whisk egg yolks. Pour the yolks into the mushroom liquid and whisk until the mixture is thick and smooth. Remove from heat and slowly add the butter, stirring until well incorporated. Spoon sauce over steaks.

Sopa de Plataños

Serves 6-8

INGREDIENTS

2 plantains, peeled and cut into 1 inch
  circles
2 t olive oil
2 T olive oil
6 cloves garlic, minced
1 large onion, finely chopped

6 cups chicken stock
1 T vinegar
1 T fresh cilantro, chopped
1 T fresh parsley, chopped
salt, pepper, and Tabasco sauce
  to taste

1. Rub plantains with 2 teaspoons olive oil and place in baking pan in preheated 350° Fahrenheit oven for 30 minutes. Remove and crush with a mallet.

2. Sauté onions and garlic in 2 tablespoons olive oil until transparent. Add crushed plantains and stock. Bring to a boil and lower to a simmer. Add vinegar, cilantro and parsley. Cook for 30 minutes and garnish with fresh cilantro.

An Extraordinary Cook
Connected to the World of Science

Dr. Harold McGee is a man of many talents who writes about the chemistry of food and cooking. He explains that he fixed on this peculiar vocation after training in three more conventional subjects: Physics and Astronomy at the California Institute of Technology, and English Literature at Yale University. His first book, "On Food and Cooking: The Science and Lore of the Kitchen" (Published in 1989 by Scribner and Harper Collins) won the André Simon Memorial Fund Book Award and brought Dr. McGee celebrity just as America was awakening to the diversity of world cuisine. His book helped to satisfy the growing hunger for information about the origins and nature of ingredients and techniques.

His next book, "The Curious Cook: More Kitchen Science and Lore" (Published in 1990 by Scribner and Harper Collins) which offers his solutions to kitchen puzzles and tries to make sense of the modern and ever-changing scientific evidence linking diet with the diseases of later life: heart disease, cancer and Alzheimer's disease. Along the way, Dr. McGee has contributed original research to "Nature" magazine and he has also written articles and reviews for many scientific and food related publications. These include a 1999 article in "Physics Today" and several articles in the "The New York Times" as well as "The World Book Encyclopedia", "Food & Wine", "Fine Cooking", and "Health". He has lectured on food chemistry to chefs and cooks all over the world and to scientists at the Fermi National Accelerator Laboratory as well as to everyone who listens to National Public Radio.

Dr. McGee and Oxford Professor Nicholas Kurti founded and organized the International Workshop on Molecular Gastronomy, held every two years in Sicily. In 1995, for his great contributions to the field, he was named to the James Beard Foundation's "Who's Who in American Food".

Chaos and Symmetry are very pleased to be able to include some of Dr. McGee's original research which first appeared in 1998 in "Nature" Magazine.

Guidelines for the Cook
(*Physics Today*, November 1999, p 36)

Our simple models for frying and immersion suggest several guidelines for maximizing the odds of cooking a succulent, evenly done piece of meat:

- Use relatively thin cuts and pre-warm them to reduce the time during which the outer portions are overcooked.
- Keep the surface temperature below the boil, so as to minimize the surface-center thermal gradient and maximize the period during which the center is within 5°C of the target. In frying and grilling, this can be done with an initial high-temperature browning followed by finishing over sparser coals or a lower flame, or by transferring the meat to the less efficient heat of the oven.
- Flip grilled and fried meats frequently. Remember that their center temperature is rising fast and there will only be a minute or two during which they're properly done. So check them often with a thermometer, a small cut, or a texture-probing poke.
- Above all, don't rely on the standard predictive formulas for cooking time in minutes per pound or per inch. Such formulas are not derived from physical principles. And, as the models demonstrate, cooking time is significantly affected by a host of variables, including initial, ambient, and cooking temperatures, irregularities in the meat's thickness, and flipping frequency. There's no substitute for direct monitoring of doneness when it comes to turning out a model of the cook's art.

Recipe for Safer Sauces

Nature, Vol 347, 25 October 1990

Contamination of intact chicken eggs by *Salmonella enteritidis* has led to a notable rise in food poisoning in the West[1-4]. Health authorities have named home-made mayonnaise, hollandaise and béarnaise sauces as dishes that pose some hazard[5]. Mayonnaise, prepared by emulsifying vegetable oil in raw egg yolks, has been implicated in several outbreaks of salmonellosis, including one at the House of Lords[6]. The acid ingredients in this sauce can eliminate salmonellae from raw yolks, but only over a period of hours to days[7]. Hollandaise and béarnaise sauces, butterfat-in-water emulsions thickened with lightly cooked yolks[8], are usually heated briefly to 70 or 75°C, but some salmonellae from an initially large population may survive this treatment[9,10]. Egg yolk seems to increase the resistance of salmonellae to thermal killing[11].

The standard kitchen method for minimizing microbial contamination, thorough boiling, has not been considered applicable to emulsified sauces. Egg yolks harden and emulsions break well below 100°C, so cooks never intentionally boil either the yolks alone or a finished sauce. But a sufficiently low pH can delay or prevent the heat coagulation of egg proteins[8,12]. Under suitable biochemical and thermal conditions, egg yolks can be boiled without curdling them or fatally compromising their ability to produce smooth, stable emulsions.

The method is as follows. Raw egg yolks are mixed thoroughly with an equal volume of water and from one-third to an equal volume of lemon juice or vinegar. This mixture is then placed in a small glass bowl, covered and irradiated in a microwave oven at maximum power until it bubbles: for 1- and 2-yolk mixtures, 1 minute or less, depending on oven power. The unevenly heated mixture is then beaten with a fresh implement and cooked a second time until it has bubbled for 5 to 10 seconds. Beaten with another fresh implement as it cools down, the yolk mixture retains the consistency of a stirred custard. I find that this mixture can then be used to make an acceptable if slightly more heat-sensitive hollandaise or béarnaise sauce or, as long as unrefined olive oil is only a small fraction of the total oil volume, a stable mayonnaise.

To test the effectiveness of this method of eliminating large bacterial populations, a culture of *S. enteritidis* strain 1601E. phange type 4 (B. A. D. Stocker, Stanford University), grown in broth with shaking for 18 hours at 37°C, was inoculated into egg yolks at about 5×10^8 colony-forming units per milliliter of yolk. The yolks, initial pH 6.2, were then mixed with water and one-third their volume of either lemon juice or vinegar; the final pH of the mixtures were 4.0 and 4.8, respectively. After an initial sample was removed, the yolk mixtures were treated as above in a Quasar microwave oven rated at 600 W, and sampled again. Bacteria were estimated by dispersing yolk samples in saline and plating dilutions on standard media. Recovery of colony-forming units from the yolks sampled before heating was consistent with the known inoculum. No live bacteria were detected in samples taken after the second heating period. The surviving population, if any, thus was probably smaller than 5 cells per milliliter of yolk.

These results suggest that cooks can greatly reduce the health risk posed by yolk-based sauces. If public-health laboratories would verify that the combination of acidification and rapid boiling reliably eliminates salmonellae from yolks, then this method could provide a more palatable alternative to abstention from freshly made mayonnaise, hollandaise and béarnaise sauces[8].

Harold McGee

1. Lancer II, 720-722 (1988).
2. Perales, I. & Audiocana A. *Lancet* il. 1133 (1988).
3. Rodrigue, D.C. Tauxe, R.V. & Rowe, B. *Epidem. Inf.* **105**, 21-27 (1990).
4. St. Louis, ME. Et al. *J. Am. Med. Ass.* **259**, 2103-2107 (1988).
5. US Centers for Disease Control *Morbidity Mortality Weekly Rept.* **38**, 877-880 (1990).
6. Glynn, A.A. *Nature* **339**, 671-672 (1989).
7. Smittle, R.B. *J. Food Protect.* **40**, 415-422 (1977).
8. McGee, H., *The Curious Cook* (North Point, San Francisco, in the press).
9. Baker, R.C. Hogarty, S. Poon, W. & Vadehra, D.V. *Poultry Sci.* **62**, 1211-1216 (1983).
10. Humphrey, T.J., Greenwood, M., Gilbert, R.J., Rowe, B & Chapman, P.A. *Epidem. Inf.* **103** 35-45 (1989).
11. Humphrey, T.J. Chapman, P.A., Rowe, B. & Gilbert, R.J. *Epidem. Inf.* **104**, 237-241 (1990).
12. Small, D.M. & Bernstein, M. *New Engl. J. Med.* **300**, 801-802 (1979).

JS.BURRUS

Why Whip Egg Whites in Copper Bowls?

Harold J. McGee*, Sharon R. Long† & Windlow R. Briggs‡

*838 La Jennifer Way, Palo Alto, California 94306, USA
†Department of Biological Sciences, Stanford University, Stanford, CA 94305, USA
‡Department of Plant Biology, Carnegie Institution of Washington, Stanford, CA 94305, USA

Foams of chicken egg albumen have been an important element in Western cuisine for at least 300 yr[1]; they lower the density of such otherwise ponderous preparations of soufflés and sponge cakes, and in the heat-annealed form known as meringues they support or crown various sucrose-rich mixtures[2]. The raw protein foam is delicate and easily ruined by overbeating. Over the past 200 yr, protocols for the production of albumen foams have frequently specified the use of copper reaction vessels[3-5]. In keeping with the line of thought that holds culinary practice to be worthy of philosophical and scientific analysis[6-8], we have investigated the nature and consequences of the copper protocol. We report here that copper utensils reduce the danger of overbeating albumen foams, and propose that the mechanism involves the metal-binding protein, conalbumin (ovotransferrin).

When the proteins are absorbed at the air-liquid interface of a foamed solution, the local imbalance of forces breaks intramolecular bonds; subsequent intermolecular bonding creates a protein film that stabilizes the foam[9]. However, if denaturation and coagulation proceed too far, the foam will drain liquid and collapse. Some resistance to surface denaturation is necessary if a protein is to produce a long-lived foam[10]. The film in foamed chicken egg white appears to involve only conalbumin, the globulins and ovomucin[11]. Conalbumin, which is homologous to the human iron-transporting protein transferin, binds Cu^{2+} as well as Fe^{3+} (refs 12, 13). Both metal-protein complexes are more resistant to various denaturing treatments than native conalbumin[13,14]. The use of copper utensils to beat egg whites could lead to formation of the copper-conalbumin complex, whose stability might prevent excessive surface denaturation and rapid foam collapse.

To test this hypothesis, we first verified that copper utensils do indeed have an effect on albumen foam stability. When 60-ml samples of egg white were beaten by hand (3-4 strokes s^{-1}) in glass or unlined copper bowls, stiff peaks[5] were obtained after 3.5-4.0 min in the former, and after 7.0 min in the latter. The sample beaten in glass became grainy within 1 min of forming stiff peaks and drained 10 ml of fluid on standing for 10 min., whereas the sample beaten 2 min past the stiff peak stage in the copper bowl had few grains, and drained only 1 ml in 20 min. Fluid loss was similarly attenuated when $CuCl_2$ (0.42 mM final concentration) was beaten with egg whites in a glass bowl.

Absorption spectra provided evidence for formation of the copper-conalbumin complex when egg whites were beaten in a copper bowl or in the presence of $CuCl_2$ (Fig. 1A). The copper-conalbumin complex is yellow and has a characteristic broad absorption band with a maximum of 439 nm[15]. When $FeCl_3$ was added to egg whites, the reported peak at 462 nm for the salmon-coloured iron-conalbumin complex was found[15]. The broad, weak absorption in the spectrum of untreated egg white is probably due to a flavorprotein[16], though a small amount of the iron complex may be present *ab ovo*.

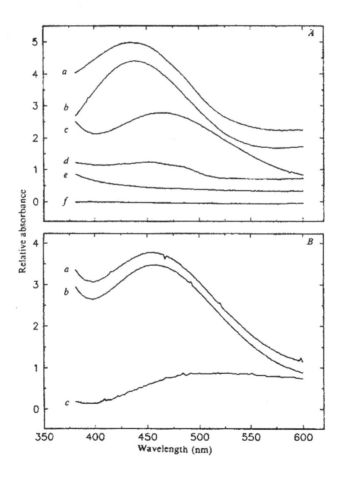

Fig. 1 The spectral behaviour of fresh egg whites beaten in various conditions. **A.** The whites of six extra large grade AA chicken eggs (Ranch Pak, San Leandro, California), pH 9.2, were mixed at 23°C; 20-ml samples were beaten briefly (2 min) with stainless whisk, and the clear, non-scattering liquid phase analysed with a Perkin-Elmer 356 spectrophotometer, interfaced with a Hewlett-Packard 1000 F Series computer. a, Unlined copper bowl (Williams-Sonoma, Palo Alto, California); b, glass bowl with added CuC12

64

(0.42 mM); c, glass bowl with added FeCl3 (0.42 mM0; f, CuCl2 (0.42 mM). Salt concentrations were based on a calculation of the total number of metal-binding sites (two per molecule of conalbumin[14]) available in egg white[22]. The curves are displaced for clarity. All spectra were close to zero absorbance of 600 nm. All curves were obtained at the same instrument sensitivity. As a reference, the maximum absorbance for curve a was near 0.5 A units. **B**. The spectral behaviour of fresh egg whites supplied with equimolar (0.42 mM) amounts of FeCl3 and CuCl2. Egg white (40 ml) was beaten briefly (2 min) with the added salt solutions. A small portion of the clear, non-scattering liquid phase was analysed (curve a) as in A. The remainder was beaten to the stiff peak stage[5], and the clear, non-scattering drainage analysed (curve peak stage[5], and the clean, non scattering drainage analysed (curve b, amplified by a factor of 4 and displaced for clarity. Maximum absorbance of curve a occurs at a wavelength ~9 nm lower than the iron-conalbumin peak in A; the maximum of curve b is ~6 nm lower. Curve c demonstrates the relative enrichment of the iron complex in the foam drainage.

In contrast to the copper-conalbumin complex, the iron-conalbumin complex is not associated with foam stabilization. Egg whites beaten with FeCl3 (0.42 mM) into stiff peaks drained fluid rapidly (13 ml in 10 min). However, when equimolar (0.42 mM) amounts of FeCl3 and CuCl2 were supplied, the resulting foam was stable (<1 ml drainage in 25 min). The composite absorbance peak (Fig. 1B) produced by this mixture demonstrates that despite an estimated disadvantage of 10^{13} in dissociation constants[17], Cu^{2+} binds to conalbumin in the presence of presumably saturating amounts of Fe^{3+}. It has been reported that Cu^{2+} reacts with the purified protein more rapidly than Fe^{3+} (refs 17, 18), though very rapid binding of Fe^{3+} has also been observed[19].

Our hypothesis requires that while the copper-conalbumin complex is more difficult to denature than the native protein, it must still be somewhat susceptible to surface denaturation in order to participate at all in the foam-stabilizing film. One possible interpretation of the disparate effects of the two metals is that the iron complex, which is considerably more stable than the copper complex[14], cannot be surface-denatured under culinary conditions, and therefore cannot play any part in foam stabilization. To test this idea, we compared the spectrum of egg whites supplied with both Fe^{3+} and Cu^{2+} with the spectrum of the drained liquid from the resulting foam (Fig. 1B). Both the difference spectrum and the shift in maximum absorbance towards the iron-complex peak indicate that the copper complex is preferentially retained in the foam.

Thus, it takes longer to beat egg whites to a given consistency in a copper bowl than it does in glass, but copper improves the foam's resistance to breakdown and so makes it more forgiving of a cook's inattention. On the basis of the spectral evidence reported here, we propose conalbumin as a possible agent for the foam-stabilizing influence of copper on egg whites. However, other albumen proteins may also be involved. Copper may react with their sulphydryl groups to form mercaptides and so interfere with their sulphydryl groups to form mercaptides and so interfere with disulphide cross-bridging (P.R. Azari, personal communication), which seems to be involved in the production of egg albumen foams[20]. Also, it is known that copper irreversibly inactivates lysozyme, one of the globulins retained in the foam, and that iron does not[21].

We thank P.R. Azari and Joseph A. Berry for helpful discussions, and Glenn Ford for assistance with data analysis. This is publication number 832 of the Department of Plant Biology, Carnegie Institution of Washington.

Revised 9 August 1983; accepted 9 February 1984.

1.   Phillips, E. The New World of English Words 6th edn (ed. Kersey, J.), S.V. Meringues (J. Phillips, London, 1706).
2.   McGee, H. On Food and Cooking. Ch. 2 (Scribner, New York, in the press).
3.   Diderot, D. & d'Alembert, J. (eds) Encyclopèdie, ou Dictionnaire Raisonnè des Sciences, des A.
4.   Escoffier, A. Guide Culinaire, 1075 (E. Colin. Paris, 1907).
5.   Child, J. Bertholle, L. & Beck, S. Mastering the Art of French Cooking Vol I. 158-259 (Kopf, New York.
6.   "Plato Gorgias, 500c-501b (Athens ~350 BC).
7.   Boswell, J. Life of Samuel Johnson Vol. 2. 205 (Dent. London, 1906).
8.   Brillat-Savarin, J. A. Physiologie du Goût. Meditation 7 (Santelet. Paris, 1826).
9.   Alexander, A.E. & Johnson, P. Colloid Science Vol. 2, 635-639 (Clarendon, Oxford, 1949).
10.   Graham, D.E. & Phillips, M.C. in Foams (ed. Akers. R.J.) 237-253 (Academic. London, 1976).
11.   Cunningham, F.E. Poultry Sci. **55**, 738-743 (1975).
12.   Fraenkel-Conrat, H. & Fenney. R.E. Archs Biochem. Biophys. **29**, 101-113 (1950).
13.   Feeney, R.E. & Allison, R.G. Evolutionary Biochemistry of Proteins. 144-171 (Wiley, New York, 1969).
14.   Azari, P.R. & Feeney, R.E. J. boil. Chem. **232**, 293-302 (1958).
15.   Komatsu, S.K. & Feeney, R.E. Biochemistry **6**, 1136-1141 (1967.
16.   Rhodes, M.B., Bennett, N. & Feeney, R.E. J. boil. Chem. **234**, 2054-2060 (1959).
17.   Warner, R.C. & Weber, I. J. Am. Chem.. Soc. **75**, 5094-5101 (1953).
18.   Tan, A.T. & Woodworth, R.C. Biochemistry **8**, 3711-3716 (1969).
19.   Williams, J., Evans, R.W. & Moreton, K. Biochem. J. **173**, 535-542 (1978).
20.   Johnson, T.M. & Zabik, M.E. J. Food Sci. **46**, 1231-1236 (1981).
21.   Feeney, R.E., MacDonnell, L.R. & Ducay, E.D. Archs Biochem. Biophys. **61**, 72-83 (1956).

Chaos and Symmetry
present recipes from

THE AMERICAS:
North and South and the Caribbean

Argentina, Brazil, Jamaica, Mexico,
And The United States of America

SS.BURRUS

A Symmetry of Fish and Flesh

Joyce Anderson, tasted by Philip Anderson, Princeton University, Princeton, NJ

Serves 6-8

INGREDIENTS

3 lb veal or pork roast
1 T oil
1 T butter
salt
pepper
garlic powder

1/3 cup white wine
1/2 cup low fat sour cream
1/2 cup mayonnaise
1 small can white tuna, in oil
1/2 t or more of dried dill weed

1. The roast would presumably be loin - in any case boneless and tied if there are floppy bits. Bones, if any can be tucked under the meat while roasting, instead of a trivet, to add flavor. Pork is best somewhat marbled and with an outer layer of fat, if such is any longer available.

2. Brown the meat over medium heat in an oven proof pan, (a skillet is good) in oil and butter, salt and pepper and sprinkle with garlic powder (the granules will be reconstituted; one could insert slivers of garlic instead).

3. Deglaze the pan with a good wash of white wine and roast the meat on a trivet (such as an 8 inch cake rack) at 300-350° Fahrenheit 40 minutes per pound for pork, 35 minutes for veal, tenting not sealing with aluminum foil. Should the liquid boil away, add water. When the meat is cooked through it shrinks visibly.

4. Remove the roast to a cutting board and let cool. Save the pan juices including the goodies from the pan bottom and skim off fat. Since the meat is cooling the pan juices can be refrigerated and the fat easily removed.

5. When the meat is no more than room temperature remove the layer of fat, if any and carve into 1/3 inch slices. Coat each slice generously with a dressing composed of the tuna, sour cream, mayonnaise and pan juices. Blend or process the tuna with the juices, then stir in first the sour cream and then the mayonnaise and the dill till smooth.

6. Build the coated slices back together and "ice" the reconstructed roast with more of the sauce (perhaps you'll remember the chocolate dessert constructed of thin cookies and whipped cream). The meat will absorb much of the sauce. Any remaining sauce can be added at serving time.

7. Refrigerate overnight or at the very least, all day. Let come to room temperature before serving.

Apple Cake

Symmetry says this is so simple that even those who do not like to bake can produce this one. Serve with whipped cream, ice cream or frozen yogurt, or nothing at all.

Serves 4

INGREDIENTS

2 eggs
2 cups sugar
1 t vanilla
1/2 cup oil
2 cups flour
2 t baking soda

2 t cinnamon
1/4 t salt
1 cup chopped nuts, pecans or walnuts
4 cups finely chopped apples, with or without skins

1. Beat eggs with sugar and vanilla until smooth, then beat in the oil.

2. In another bowl mix the flour, baking soda, cinnamon and salt.

3. Combine the two mixtures and fold in the nuts and apples. Spoon into the buttered baking pan and bake at 350° Fahrenheit for about 1 hour.

Note: at an altitude over 6,000 ft., use less baking soda.

Black-Eyed Peas
with Seasonal Greens

CHAOS at Duke University

Serves 6

INGREDIENTS

3 cups fresh or frozen black-eyed peas
1-1/2 quarts chicken broth
1/2 lb country ham, cut in cubes
salt and freshly ground pepper

3 cups of broth as made below
1 onion, chopped
2 t black pepper corns

Combine the peas with the ham and the broth and simmer over medium heat until tender, about 1 hour. Season with salt and pepper.

Seasonal Greens
Makes 6 servings

3 cups ham broth

2 lb collard, turnip or mustard greens

Slice greens into 1 inch ribbons and add to the boiling pot of broth. Simmer for about 20 minutes, drain and serve together with the black-eyed peas and ham.

BBQ Chicken

Nancy Fried, tasted by Herbert Fried, Brown University

Serves 4

INGREDIENTS

1 chicken
pepper
garlic
salt
oregano

Sauce:
2 cups burgundy wine
1 cup olive oil
1 T oregano
pinch of salt
1/2 t coarsely ground
 black pepper
1 t garlic powder

1. Heat sauce ingredients to boiling, but do not let it boil.

2. Cut chicken into pieces for barbecuing, skin can be removed.

3. Rub pieces with pepper, garlic, salt and oregano.

4. Barbecue chicken. As soon as it is taken off the grill, dip the pieces into and out of the sauce.

Beef Pasta and Artichokes

CHAOS thinks this very simple salad can be enjoyed at the traditional
Tuesday picnics at the Center for Physics

Serves 6

INGREDIENTS

1-1/2 lb sirloin steaks
1 can quartered artichoke bottoms
1 large red pepper cut into strips
1 cup pitted ripe olives
2 T fresh basil, chopped
4 cups pasta of choice,
   cooked "al dente"

Vinaigrette:
1/4 cup virgin olive oil
1 large lemon, juice only
1 T dijon mustard
salt and freshly ground black pepper
   to taste

1, Broil steak, slice, and add everything else in a bowl.

2. Add vinaigrette and chill for 2 hours or overnight.

Best Marinade

CHAOS combined the following and uses the result to marinate
chicken, turkey, pork or fish

Double or triple as needed

INGREDIENTS

juice of one lemon
1/2 cup olive oil
3 T soy sauce
2 T mustard (the "Dijon" imported
from France is the best)
3 large cloves garlic, crushed

1 t dried oregano (the Mediterranean is
best)
3 t dried basil
1 t crushed red pepper
1 t crushed black pepper

1. Whisk together all the above ingredients and use as marinade or as basting sauce for grilled turkey tenderloins, chicken breasts, pork tenderloins or chops, skewered cubes of meat, fish or scallops, or anything else you might think of doing with it.

Carrot Souffle

Symmetry discovered a souffle that never falls!

Serves 8

INGREDIENTS

2 cups cooked and pureed carrots
1 T lemon juice
1 T grated onion
1/4 cup unsalted butter
1/4 cup sugar

1 T flour
1 t salt
1/4 t cinnamon
1 cup milk
3 eggs

Beat all the above together. Pour into 2 quart buttered souffle dish and bake at 350°Fahrenheit for about 1 hour.

Cheese and Wine Bread

Carol Ann Jacobson, Aspen, Colorado

Makes 1 Large Loaf

INGREDIENTS

3 cups all-purpose flour
1 package active dry yeast
1/2 cup dry white wine
1/2 cup butter

2 t sugar
1 t salt
3 eggs
1 cup (4 oz) cubed monterey jack cheese

1.   In large mixer bowl combine 1-1/2 cups of flour and yeast. In saucepan, heat wine, butter sugar and salt just until warm (115° to 120° Fahrenheit), stirring constantly until butter almost melts. Add to dry mixture in mixer bowl. Add eggs. Beat at low speed of electric mixer for 1 to 2 minutes, scraping sides of bowl constantly.

2.   Beat 3 minutes at high speed.   By hand, stir in the cheese and enough remaining flour to make a soft dough. Turn out on lightly floured surface, knead until smooth and elastic. Place in lightly greased bowl, turning once to grease surface. Cover and let rise in warm place until double, about 1-1/2 hours. Punch dough down; cover and let rest 10 minutes. Shape into an 8-inch round loaf.

3.   Place in greased 9-inch pie plate, cover and let rise in warm place until double, about 40 minutes. Bake at 375° Fahrenheit for about 40 minutes, covering with aluminum foil after the first 20 minutes of baking.

Note: In Aspen, bake the bread for about 1 hour to be sure it is completely baked through and crusty. Also, you can use a mixer with a dough hook and add the cheese and remaining flour with the mixer at its lowest speed, rather than stirring by hand.

Chicken Piccata

This contribution comes from writers J. Barnard and M. Fain, Aspen, Colorado

Serves 4

INGREDIENTS

4 skinless, boneless chicken breast
  halves

Sauce:
1/4 cup lemon juice
1/4 cup chicken broth
4 T capers
1/4 cup chopped parsley
3 T butter
1-1/2 T flour
2 T olive oil
1/3 cup dry white wine

1. Pound chicken between sheets of plastic wrap to about 1/4 inch thickness. Salt and pepper lightly and dip into 1-1/2 T of flour shaking off excess.

2. Sauté chicken in olive oil until cooked through, about 3 minutes per side. Keep warm covered with aluminum foil.

3. Boil wine, lemon juice and chicken broth, whisk in butter flour mixture and boil until mixture thickens slightly, about 2-3 minutes. Add capers, parsley and 2 tablespoons butter, season to taste with salt and pepper. Pour sauce over chicken and serve.

Chicken with Salsa and Pecans

Symmetry does not remember where the original came from. Many variations exist, but this one is truly tasty and easy to prepare. Serve with rice, white or wild, couscous, spaetzle or orzo pasta.

Serves 4

INGREDIENTS

1 T olive oil
1/2 cup pecans
3 garlic cloves
4 boneless and skinless chicken breasts
1 1/2 cup salsa

4 T dried currants
2 T dried cranberries
1 t cumin
1/2 t cinnamon, or to taste
1 T chopped cilantro

1. Brown pecans in olive oil for a few minutes and remove to a dish. Add garlic to the skillet. After a few minutes add the chicken breasts and cook until browned.

2. Combine all remaining ingredients, mix well and add to chicken. Reduce heat and cook, covered, for about 20 minutes.

3. Stir in toasted pecans, sprinkle with cilantro and serve.

Chili Verde (Green Chile with Pork)

Contributed by Carla and tasted by R. Stephen Berry, University of Chicago
This is a hearty stew which is a wonderful warmer-upper after skiing or on a cold
wintry day. It can be made with beef instead of pork, if you prefer. The seasonings
can be zapped up to the heat which you enjoy. The secret is the plentiful use of
green chilies. Serve as a soup or over rice. Extra garnishes can include guacamole
and sour cream. Accompany with warm flour tortillas.

Serves 8

INGREDIENTS

2 lbs pork shoulder cut into
   inch cubes
2 lbs country style pork ribs
   with bones
3 T olive oil
2 large onions, chopped
1 green pepper chopped
2 garlic cloves, minced
1 large can whole tomatoes
6 cans (7 oz) chopped green chilies
1 T red chili powder

1 laurel leaf
2 jalapeno peppers (seeded and chopped)
1/4 cup cilantro chopped
1/4 cup parsley
1/4 t ground cloves
2 T oregano
2-3 T ground cumin
1 cup white wine
3 cups chicken broth
1 large can hominy
salt and pepper to taste

1. Dust meat with flour and brown in oil, in batches. Drain on paper towel and reserve.

2. In the drippings sauté green pepper, jalapenos, onion and garlic until soft. Add oil as needed.

3. In a large kettle heat tomatoes, green chilies, wine and broth.

4. Add onion and pepper mixture and the meat to the kettle. Add seasonings. Cover and simmer for 2 hours. Remove any bones and laurel leaf.

5. This dish is best made the day before. Chill. At serving time, remove any fat on the surface. Slowly reheat. Add the hominy. Simmer and adjust seasonings. **OLE!**

Chimichurri

This traditional Argentinian sauce is served with grilled or roasted meats.
A Symmetry discovery.

Makes 1-1/2 cups

INGREDIENTS

1/2 cup olive oil
1/4 cup red wine vinegar
1/2 cup chopped onions
1 t chopped garlic
1/4 cup chopped parsley

1 t oregano
1/4 t Cayenne pepper
1-1/2 t salt
1 t freshly ground black pepper

Beat together the oil and vinegar and then add all other ingredients. Let the sauce
stand at room temperature for several hours in order to develop its flavor.

Chocolate Mousse

This recipe was contributed by Marjorie Appel,
Jeff Appel at Fermi Lab was the official taster.

Serves 12 or more

INGREDIENTS

1/2 lb sweet chocolate*
6 large eggs, separated
3 T water
1/2 cup sweet liqueur, Amaretto**

2 cups heavy cream
6 T sugar
whipped cream for garnish
grated chocolate for garnish

1. Cut the chocolate into half-inch pieces and place the chocolate in a sauce pan. Set the saucepan in hot, almost boiling water and cover. Let melt over low heat.

2. Put yolks in a heavy saucepan over very low heat while beating vigorously and constantly with a wire whisk. Experienced cooks may do this over direct heat such as a low flame or electric burner. It may be preferable, however, to use a metal disk such as a Flame-Tamer to control the heat. In any event, when the yolks start to thicken, add the liqueur, beating constantly. Cook until the sauce achieves the consistency of a hollandaise or sabayon, which it is. Remove from heat.

3. Add the melted chocolate to the sauce in a mixing bowl. Beat the cream until stiff, adding 2 tablespoons of the sugar towards the end of the beating. Fold this into the chocolate mixture. Beat the whites until soft peaks start to form. Beat in the remaining sugar and continue beating until stiff. Fold this into the mousse. Spoon the mousse into a crystal bowl and chill until ready to serve. Garnish with whipped cream and grated chocolate.

* Or Semi-Sweet
** Other liqueurs that can be used: Chartreuese, Mandarine or Grand Marnier

75

Chorizo and Scallops

A trip to Cape Cod by Symmetry yielded this recipe

Serves 6

INGREDIENTS

1 lb sea scallops
*1 lb chorizo sausage, sliced to conform
   to scallop size*
*1 bunch of green onions, sliced into
   1 inch pieces*

1/2 t garlic, minced
1/2 cup good quality dry white wine
1/4 cup clam juice
*1 T extra virgin olive oil salt and freshly
   ground black pepper*

1. Heat oil. Add chorizo and cook until browned. Transfer to serving dish and keep warm.

2. Wipe out the skillet and add 1 tablespoon olive oil. Season scallops and cook over high heat, turning once until golden (about 3 minutes). Add scallops to chorizo plate.

3. Heat olive oil and add the green onions and the garlic and sauté about 2 minutes. Pour in wine and boil until almost evaporated, scraping the bottom of the pan to loosen the brown bits. Pour in the clam juice, if you are using it, and reduce the liquid by half. Pour sauce over chorizo and scallops and serve. For thicker sauce, add a little flour, corn starch or butter to the wine.

Cornish Game Hens

Betty Shermer as tasted by Lloyd Shermer, Aspen, Colorado

Serves 8

INGREDIENTS

8 Cornish game hens
1 cup olive oil
4 T fresh lemon juice
salt and pepper to taste
16 sprigs fresh basil

8 T Dijon mustard
4 T balsamic vinegar
8 cloves garlic, minced or crushed
1-1/4 T Herbes de Provence

1. Rinse hens and pat dry. Mix oil and lemon juice, pour over hens in a large bowl and marinate for 3 to 4 hours, turning often. Remove hens from marinade and save both.

2. Salt and pepper the hens inside and out, put 2 sprigs of basil in the cavity of each hen, rub each hen with 1 tablespoon of Dijon mustard and place in roasting pan. Heat oven to 450° Fahrenheit and roast hens for 15 minutes.

3. Combine reserved marinade, vinegar, garlic and Herbes de Provence. Reduce oven temperature to 350° Fahrenheit and continue roasting the hens for 1 hour, basting them frequently with the combined liquid.

P.S. You may roast the hens for 45 minutes to 1 hour early in the day, and just before serving, brown them well over a charcoal grill: they may be served at room temperature or packed in a chilled container in a cooler to take on a picnic.

Cocktail Meatballs in Sweet and Sour Sauce

CHAOS feels that these are delicious and so simple to prepare for a large crowd

Serves 8 as appetizers

INGREDIENTS

In a pot put:
2 cups boiling water, then:
1/2 cup white raisins
1/2 cup brown sugar
1-1/2 sliced lemons
1 cup ketchup
1 cup chili sauce
2 t "Kitchen Bouquet"
2 t paprika

The meatballs:
2 lb ground meat (beef, veal, or turkey)
1 medium onion, grated
1 egg
1 cup dry bread crumbs
salt and freshly ground pepper to taste

Form the meatballs about the size of a walnut and add these to the simmering liquid. When the last meatball has been added, simmer another 3-4 minutes. Serve in a chafing dish.

Couscous Salad

A change from pasta or potato salad
for those Tuesday picnics by Symmetry.

Serves 12

INGREDIENTS

2 cups couscous
1 cup shredded carrot
1 cup shredded turnip
2 cups diced tomatoes
1 cup diced peeled apple
1 can drained and rinsed chick peas

1 cup diced green onions
1/2 cup chopped fresh cilantro
2 T minced garlic
1/4 cup olive oil
4 lemons, juice and grated rind
salt and freshly ground pepper

Bring 3 cups of water to boil and stir in the couscous, remove from heat, cover and let rest for 5-8 minutes. Add the carrots and turnips, stir and let cool, uncovered. Add everything else and blend. Adjust seasoning to taste.

Couscous with Currants

Symmetry thinks this is a fine dish to take to a Tuesday physics picnic.

Serves 8

INGREDIENTS

2 cups couscous
1/2 cup dried currants
1/2 t salt or more to taste
6 ripe plum tomatoes
3 cloves garlic, chopped

1/4 cup fresh lemon juice
1 t brown Dijon mustard
1 bunch finely chopped scallions
1/2 cup parsley, chopped
freshly ground black pepper to taste

1. In a large bowl, stir together 3 cups lukewarm water, couscous, currants and salt. Let stand for 30 minutes, or until the water has been absorbed and the couscous is tender. Meanwhile, dip the tomatoes into boiling water for a few seconds, refresh under cold water and slip off the skins. Cut the tomatoes in half crosswise, remove seeds, dice and set aside.

2. Heat a heavy skillet over medium heat. Add garlic and cook for about 10 minutes. In a blender or food processor combine lemon juice, olive oil, mustard and roasted garlic. Blend until smooth. Season with salt and pepper. Fluff the couscous with a fork. Add scallions, parsley and diced tomatoes. Drizzle with the lemon dressing and toss lightly to coat. Taste and adjust seasoning. Serve within 2 hours.

Curried Carrots

Contributed by Sarah Brett-Smith of Rutgers University,
as tasted by Stephen Adler, Institute for Advanced Study.
You need at least an hour of time and a very large, deep saucepan with a good lid.

Serves 8

INGREDIENTS

3 lbs carrots
3-4 large onions
1/4-1/2 cup olive oil and vegetable oil
  (you may need a little more oil)
4 cloves garlic, finely chopped
2 pieces ginger root, finely chopped

2-3 T ground cumin
2-3 T ground coriander
1/2 t curry powder
2 T soy sauce
1 lemon, juice only

1. Peel and thinly slice carrots. Heat oil until very hot and sauté, then add the spices and chopped carrots and continue cooking until they are partially browned.

2. Now add onions, soy sauce and lemon juice and keep stirring. The dish is done in about 20 minutes but, if you like, you can cook it longer. The longer it "stews," the tastier the dish. This keeps for about 1 week in the refrigerator and improves with age. Do not freeze.

Fancy String Beans

Contributed by Rita Block as tasted by Robert Block, Rensselaer Polytechnic Institute

Serves 6

INGREDIENTS

1 lb or more of fresh green beans
1 large red pepper
1 or 2 large sweet onions
slivered almonds, toasted

spices to taste:
lemon pepper
salt
dill weed
garlic powder
butter
curled parsley
salt

1. Mix spices together and set aside.

2. Cook beans in a small amount of water, for about 4 minutes (they should be firm).

3. Sauté pepper and onions in butter until just limp.

4. Drain beans and add the pepper and onion mixture and the spices. Add a bit more butter and only enough water for heating later.

5. Garnish with toasted slivered almonds and parsley.

Feijoada

Eduardo Gregores, University of Wisconsin, Madison and Brazil

Serves 15

INGREDIENTS

1 lb thick cut bacon,
* cut into 1 inch sections*
4 garlic cloves
1 very large onion
3 lb black beans (rinsed)
4 laurel leaves
salt to taste

1 lb carne seca or corned beef
3-4 smoked pork hocks
1 lb pork loin
1 lb kielbasa, sliced
1 lb Italian or German sausage, sliced
steamed rice

1. In a huge stock pot, at least 10 quarts, fry the bacon until crisp. Add the onion and garlic and brown. Drain off all the excess fat.

2. Add the beans and laurel leaves and 4 quarts of water. Bring to a boil over high heat, add salt, and then simmer over reduced heat for about 1½ hours. Keep covered with water at all times.

3. Add all the meat, but not the sausages and simmer for another 2 hours, adding water as needed to keep everything covered.

4. Remove the meat, trim off all excess fat and gristle and cut it into cubes, then return it to the pot. Add the sausages and continue to simmer until the beans are cooked through and the sauce is creamy.

5. Adjust the seasoning to taste. Serve over steamed rice.

Garnishes for Feijoada Completa: Orange wedges or slices, Sautèed Collard greens, Farofa de Mangeiga, Molho de pimenta e Limao, Arroz Brasileiro.

Farofa de Manteiga (toasted Manioc meal)

2 T butter
1/2 large peeled onion, thinly sliced
1 egg, lightly beaten
1-1/3 cup manioc meal

1 T chopped parsley
4 pimento stuffed olives, sliced
2-4 hard boiled eggs, halved
1 t salt

Heat butter, drop in sliced onion and cook until soft. Pour in the beaten egg. Stir in manioc meal and cook for 8 minutes. Stir in salt and parsley. Garnish with olives and eggs. Serve hot or at room temperature.

Molho de Pimenta e Limao

4 bottled Tabasco peppers, drained
* and finely chopped*
1/2 cup chopped onions

1/4 T garlic, chopped
1/2 cup fresh lemon juice

Combine everything and marinate at room temperature for 1 hour before serving.

Arroz Brasileiro

1/4 cup olive oil
1 large onion, sliced
3 cups raw rice
3 cups boiling chicken stock

3 cups boiling water
2 tomatoes, peeled,
* seeded and chopped*
1 t salt

Heat oil, add anion, when soft add rice.   After several minutes add stock, tomatoes, salt and water. Return to boil and steam gently for 20 minutes.

Fruit Tarte

Andrea Stryer as tasted by Lubert Stryer, Stanford University

Serves 6

INGREDIENTS

Crust:
1 cup toasted almonds
zest of 1/2 an orange or lemon
1/2 cup flour
1/4 lb butter, cut into slices
2 T orange juice
apricot or currant jam

Filling:
3 cups fresh fruit
1 large apple or pear
2 T sugar
lemon

Crust:

1. Process nuts with orange or lemon peel until rather fine. Add flour and butter. Process until just blended.

2. Add orange juice and process. Blend until it comes together in a ball, adding a little more juice, if necessary. Chill.

3. Roll out and place in pie pan. Weight the dough (use pie weights, rice, or beans on parchment or aluminum foil) and bake at 425° Fahrenheit for 15 minutes. Remove weight. Spread apricot or currant jam to "waterproof" the crust. return to oven for 8-10 minutes, until golden brown.

Filling:

1. Peel the apple or pear, slice, and squeeze lemon over it, add sugar, cook until soft and mash (or use applesauce). Spread on baked crust.

2. In summer, place fresh berries, peaches, apricots, or plums. In winter, sliced, lightly cooked apples or pears. Sprinkle with sliced almonds.

Ginger Pumpkin Soup with Shitake Mushrooms

Kathleen Beasley, tasted by Steven Block, Stanford University
This is a delicious autumn soup.

Serves 8

INGREDIENTS

3 quarts chicken stock
1 medium pumpkin or butternut squash
  or one large can of pumpkin
2 T chopped fresh garlic
24 medium shitake mushrooms
1 T fresh ginger, minced
2 t ground powdered ginger

1 pint of non-fat buttermilk
4 ounces honey
1 lemon
1 pinch ground allspice
black pepper to taste
4 leaves fresh basil,
  thinly sliced for garnish

1. Cut the pumpkin into four quarters and remove all the seeds and inner fibers. (A grapefruit knife is an ideal tool for this task). Place the pumpkin pieces skin-side down on a cookie sheet and roast in a preheated 350° Fahrenheit oven for 30 minutes.

2. Remove all the skin and cut the pumpkin into two-inch squares. Place the pumpkin with the garlic, ginger and 1 cup of the chicken stock in a 4-quart stock pot and cook over low heat for 10 minutes. Add the remaining stock and bring to a boil. Turn the heat down to low and simmer until the pumpkin is tender, about 30 minutes.

3. Add all the remaining ingredients except the mushrooms. Puree the mixture in a food processor until it is smooth, then pour it back into the stock pot and bring it to a simmer on low heat.

4. Remove the stems from the shitake mushrooms and cut them into ¼ inch slices. Add these to the soup and simmer for 2 more minutes. To serve, ladle into serving bowls and garnish with sliced basil.

Grilled Pork Tenderloin with North Carolina BBQ Sauce

A long time ago CHAOS lived in North Carolina
and this was a favorite with some faculty members at Duke University

Serves 6

INGREDIENTS

3 lb pork tenderloin, trimmed of fat
1 t Worcestershire sauce
1 t freshly ground black pepper

North Carolina Barbecue Sauce:
1 cup distilled white vinegar
4 t kosher salt
1 t freshly ground black pepper
1 t red pepper flakes
1 t ground red pepper
   (cayenne)

1. Brush tenderloins with Worcestershire sauce and pepper. Place in a shallow dish and marinate in refrigerator for 2-8 hours. Grill the meat to 150° Fahrenheit (this takes about 15 minutes on a charcoal or gas grill) and serve with the North Carolina Sauce.

2. To make the sauce, combine all ingredients in a glass jar with a tight fitting lid and shake well. Make the sauce several days before using it in order to mellow it.

Heartstoppingly Delicious Chocolate Sauce

Virgil Barnes, Purdue University approved by Linda Barnes

INGREDIENTS

1 stick salted butter
1/2 cup cocoa powder
1/2 to 2/3 cup moist brown sugar

1-3 T milk
ice cream

1. Melt butter over low heat, taking care not to let it bubble or clarify. Add the cocoa powder and brown sugar and stir together until just blended.

2. Stir in milk, in stages, stopping at desired consistency. It should flow enough to partly coat a serving of ice cream, when spooned on. Heat, but do not cook the mixture. The sugar should remain slightly granular, not completely dissolved.

Honey Lavender Sauce

As recommended by Bill Gruenberg, Aspen Colorado. Great on salmon!

INGREDIENTS

3 T sesame oil
1 heaping T garlic, chopped
1 heaping T ginger, chopped
3 T green onions, chopped
2 T dry lavender flowers
1/2 t Korean chili

6 T rice vinegar
7 T honey
4-1/2 T soy sauce
3 T oriental barbecue sauce
1 T hoisin sauce

1. Sauté the garlic, ginger, green onion, 1 tablespoon lavender and chili in sesame oil.

2. Add the rice vinegar, honey, soy sauce, barbecue sauce and hoisin sauce. Stir and bring to a boil. Reduce heat and simmer 20 minutes.

3. Thicken with a little cornstarch. Stir in remaining lavender and let cool. Reheat as needed.

Hearty Minestrone Soup

Contributed by Carla Berry, Early Childhood educator, Roosevelt University

Serves 10

INGREDIENTS

1/2 cup kidney beans
1/2 lb bacon
1/4 lb Italian sausage or pepperoni
2 cloves garlic to taste
1 onion
2 stalks celery
1 zucchini
1 leek
Parmesan cheese (imported)

1 t allspice
2 T basil
1 laurel leaf
8 cups soup stock
2 cups shredded cabbage
1 cup red wine
1 large can crushed tomatoes
1/2 cup macaroni or other firm pasta
salt and pepper to taste

1. Soak the beans overnight in cold water. If possible, use Roman beans.

2. In a heavy skillet, brown the chopped bacon, sausage or pepperoni and garlic. Add the chopped onion, celery, leek, sliced zucchini and seasonings. Simmer 10 minutes.

3. In a large soup kettle, heat the soup stock and add the contents of the skillet. Add the drained beans, cabbage and red wine. Simmer for about 1 1/2 hours. Add the tomatoes and macaroni. Cook until the pasta is done. Serve with garnish of basil and cheese.

Jerk Chicken

Contributed by Randy and Bernice Durand of the University of Wisconsin
Serve with rice and marinade sauce, mango salsa (preferred) or Pico de Gallo, sweet
corn bread and a light green salad.

Serves 4

INGREDIENTS

*4-6 half chicken breasts, boneless and
    skinless
1 medium red onion, finely diced
1 garlic clove, finely diced
3-4 T oil
2-3 T soy sauce
1 t grated ginger
1 t grated cinnamon*

*1 t ground allspice
1/2 t freshly ground black
    pepper
2-3 serrano peppers (depending on
    heat) very finely diced
a few drops of Tabasco
1-2 T fresh cilantro leaves, chopped
    for garnish*

Mix all ingredients except cilantro in a large bowl. Thoroughly coat the chicken with the mixture and marinate for at least 2 hours (overnight is fine). Grill the chicken very hot until just done (still barely pink but firm, very juicy: it will continue to cook off the grill). Sprinkle with chopped cilantro to serve.

Sauce for rice:

Sauté leftover marinade briefly. Add about 1 cup of chicken broth, cook until onions are translucent and adjust thickness.

Mango Salsa:

Combine and serve at room temperature:

*1 large ripe mango, diced into about 1/8 inch cubes, with juice
4 T finely diced sweet red pepper
2 T chopped fresh cilantro leaves
1 serrano pepper, very finely diced
1/2 lime, juice only*

Lemon Bars

Contributed by Paula Ruderman, tasted by Mal Ruderman, Columbia University

Serves 4

INGREDIENTS

1/2 lb butter
2 cup flour
4 T sugar
(these form the base)

4 eggs
2 cups sugar
3 large lemons, juice only and the
grated rind of one of the lemons
4 T flour

1. In a food processor, place softened butter, flour and sugar. Process until ingredients form a ball. Spread this dough evenly on bottom of a large rectangular pan and bake for 20 minutes at 325° Fahrenheit.

2. Combine eggs and sugar well with hand beater, add rind and juice of lemons. Add flour. Pour on top of dough and bake at 350° Fahrenheit until this filling is firm. When cool, it will firm up more. Cut into squares and dust with powdered sugar.

Lima Bean Puree

Contributed by Jane Frazer, as tasted by William Frazer, University of California

INGREDIENTS

1 package frozen lima beans
1/3-1/2 cup extra virgin olive oil
2 cloves garlic, peeled and
*   chopped fine*

1 small sprig rosemary
1 small sprig thyme
1/2 lemon

1. Simmer lima beans about half as long as you normally would. Drain.

2. Warm about 1/4 cup of the oil in a shallow, nonreactive pan. Add the beans, garlic and herbs. Salt lightly and add a splash of water. Cook at a slow simmer for about 30 minutes, stirring frequently, until they are completely soft. Add splashes of water as necessary to prevent the beans from sticking to the pan. Keep at low heat to keep the beans from turning brown.

3. Discard the herbs and puree the beans using a food mill or food processor (or blender if that's all that's available). Add more salt and olive oil and a few drops of lemon juice to taste. If the puree is too dry, add more oil.

4. Serve at room temperature on toasted slices of a good baguette. Keeps for up to a week in the refrigerator.

Louisiana Pecan Pie

Both these Louisiana recipes are by Marion Weiss, as tasted by Don Weiss, Shreveport, LA

Serves 4

INGREDIENTS

1 unbaked 9" pie crust
3 eggs
1-1/2 cups light Karo syrup
3/4 cup sugar

1/8 t salt
1-1/2 t vanilla
3 T butter, melted
1-1/2 cups pecan halves

Beat eggs, add Karo, butter, vanilla and salt. Pour into unbaked crust. Bake 10 minutes at 450° Fahrenheit then reduce heat to 325° Fahrenheit and bake 35-45 minutes until pie seems set when shaken. Center does not have to be stiff.

Louisiana Style Stuffed Eggplant

Serves 4

INGREDIENTS

2 large eggplants, halved
   lengthwise
salted water to cover
1/2 cup chopped onions
1/2 cup chopped green onions
2-3 cloves garlic, minced
1/2 cup chopped green pepper
1/4 cup chopped celery
1 laurel leaf
1/2 t thyme
salt to taste (1-2 teaspoons)
1/2 t black pepper
2 T olive oil

1-1/2 lb raw shrimp peeled,
   if large cut into 1/2" pieces
2 T butter
1/4 t Tabasco
1/2 T Worcestershire sauce
2 slices stale bread, crumbled
1 egg, beaten
1/4 cup chopped parsley
1/2 lb fresh crabmeat (if unavailable,
   increase shrimp)
1/2 pint raw oysters, drained
4 T grated Romano cheese
1 tomato, peeled, seeded and cut up

1. Boil eggplant halves in salted water for about 10 minutes or until tender. Scoop out insides and chop. Place shells in shallow baking dish.

2. In a Dutch oven, sauté onions, green onions, garlic, green pepper, laurel leaves, thyme, salt and pepper in olive oil for about 15 minutes. Add chopped eggplant and continue cooking over a low fire for another 15 minutes. Add shrimp, butter, Tabasco, Worcestershire, bread and egg. The oysters should be cooked separately until the edges curl and drain off liquid, then add.

3. Stir in parsley, crabmeat and lemon juice and blend gently. Remove laurel leaf. Fill shells. Sprinkle each with 1 tablespoon Romano cheese and bake at 350° Fahrenheit until hot and brown on top, about 30 minutes. Can be made ahead and frozen, either before baking or after (but best before).

Serve with a green salad of choice and corn on the cob and/or French bread. Serve pecan pie for dessert.

Matambre

This stuffed and rolled flank steak is part of the Symmetry collection from Argentina

Serves 10 servings as an hors d'oeuvre

INGREDIENTS

2 two lb flank steaks
1/2 cup red wine vinegar
1 t garlic, chopped
1 t thyme

Stuffing:
1/2 lb fresh spinach
8 cleaned and cooked whole carrots
  (6-8 inches long and 1 inch diameter)

4 hard boiled eggs cut lengthwise into
  quarters
1 large onion, sliced and divided into
  rings
1/4 cup chopped parsley
1 t crushed chili peppers
1 T coarse salt
3 cups beef broth
1-3 cups water

1. Butterfly the flank steaks and marinate with the vinegar, garlic and thyme in the refrigerator overnight.

2. Lay the steaks, cut side up, end-to-end so they overlap by about 2 inches. Pound the joint ends together. Spread the washed spinach leaves over the meat and arrange the carrots in parallel rows and place the eggs in between the carrots. Place the onion rings on top and scatter with salt, chili and parsley. Roll the steaks into a thick cylinder and tie the meat at 1 inch intervals with strong kitchen twine.

3. Place the Matambre in a casserole or roasting pan and cover with broth and water. Cover tightly and roast in a 375˚ Fahrenheit oven for about 1 hour. Remove from roaster and press under weights until cool. Slice into 1/4 inch slices after it is cooled in the refrigerator. Serve cold.

Mustard Shrimp Á La Chaos

Simple, fast and good.

Serves 6

INGREDIENTS

2 lb cooked frozen shrimp
4 T mustard (Maille)
1/2 cup very mild white wine
  vinegar

5 T chopped shallots
5 T chopped parsley
1/2 cup virgin olive oil
salt and pepper to taste

Place frozen shrimp in a ceramic bowl. Whisk together all the rest, except the vinegar and mustard, to make a creamy sauce, and pour over the shrimp. Cover and refrigerate overnight. Just before serving, whisk together the vinegar and mustard and add to the sauce. This procedure will keep the shrimp from getting rubbery. Serve with toothpicks.

Pasta and Sun-Dried Tomatoes, Olives and Goat Cheese

Carol Auvil as tasted by Paul Auvil, Northwestern University

Serves 2

INGREDIENTS

2 large minced garlic cloves
3/4 cup finely chopped onion
2 T olive oil
2/3 cup sun-dried tomatoes,
   packed in oil
1/2 cup chicken broth

1/4 cup sliced, pitted Kalamata olives
1/3 cup finely chopped fresh parsley
8 oz chevre (goat cheese) plus extra
   to sprinkle on top before serving
1/2 lb pasta

1. Cook garlic, onion, salt and pepper to taste in olive oil over moderately low heat, stirring until onion is soft. Add tomatoes and broth and simmer until liquid is reduced by one third. Stir in olives, parsley and more salt and pepper if needed. Set aside and keep warm.

2. Cook pasta "al dente," drain and reserve 1/3 cup cooking water. In the serving bowl, whisk the chevre with the cooking water until cheese is melted and mixture is smooth. Add pasta and tomato mixture and toss. Sprinkle each serving with additional crumbled cheese.

Note: Double the tomato mixture if 1 lb of pasta is used.

Paté a la Chaos

This is a CHAOS invention for a low-fat diet: no meat, butter, or egg yolks.

Serves 12

INGREDIENTS

Main Ingredients:
1 lb pecans
3-4 large onions
6 hard-boiled eggs (whites only)
1 large can peas, drained
   (approx. 15 oz)
1 6 oz can mushrooms, drained
2 oz olive oil
2 t dry mustard
2 t curry powder
2 t quatre épice (a mixture of
   equal quantities ground cinnamon,
   ginger, cloves and nutmeg)

1/4 cup cognac
salt and pepper
3 T Knox gelatin
1/4 cup rinsed green pepper corns

Aspic Ingredients:
3 T plain gelatin
2 cups chicken or beef broth
1 cup dry white wine

Garnish:
Laurel leaves, red pimentos, black
   and green olives.

1. To make layer of aspic, dissolve gelatin in a mixture of 1 cup broth and 1/2 cup white wine. Line 2 paté molds with a layer of aspic and set aside to chill until firm.

2. Dice and sauté onions in olive oil. When onions are limp, fold in the mustard, curry powder and quatre épice, plus salt and freshly ground pepper to taste. Throw onions, hard boiled egg whites, peas and mushrooms into the food processor and process until you get the consistency you want.

3. Add the ground pecans. You may have to add a little more olive oil to make it smoother. To this mixture add the cognac.

4. Fold in 3 tablespoons gelatin that have been dissolved in 1/2 cup cold water. Finally, fold in 1/4 cup or more of the rinsed green pepper corns.

5. Now, place this mixture on the two solidified aspics and chill. Garnish each mold with strips of red pimento and make patterns with black and green olives and laurel leaves. Chill.

6. When everything is firm, repeat the procedure in step 1 above and coat the entire dish with another layer of aspic. Chill thoroughly. For a firmer aspic, adjust the quantity of water to gelatin.

Peach and Blueberry Cobbler

Betty Schermer as tasted by Lloyd Schermer, Aspen, Colorado

Serves 8
Recipe may be doubled and baked in a 9"x 13" pan

INGREDIENTS

1-1/2 lbs fresh peaches, pitted, peeled
   and sliced
1 1-1/2 pints blueberries, rinsed and
   picked over
2 t cornstarch
1/2 cup sugar
1/2 cup flour

1/2 t cinnamon
pinch of ground cloves
1/4 t baking powder
pinch of salt
1 stick unsalted, softened butter
1 egg yolk
1/4 t vanilla

1. Place fruit in a large bowl and add cornstarch, 1/2 cup sugar, 1 teaspoon vanilla, cinnamon and ground cloves. Mix fruit gently and place in an 8 inch square or 9 inch round pan.

2. To make the topping, mix flour, baking powder, and salt in a small bowl and set aside.

3. Beat the butter and sugar until well blended. Beat in egg yolk and vanilla. Add flour mixture and stir until well combined. Drop large spoonfuls of the topping on the fruit mixture (it will spread while baking). Bake on a cookie sheet in a 375° Fahrenheit oven until brown, about 45-55 minutes. Serve slightly warm or at room temperature with ice cream, frozen yogurt or whipped cream.

Peach Chutney

Carla Berry, tasted and approved
by R. Stephen Berry, University of Chicago

Makes 6-8 small jars, depending on the size used

INGREDIENTS

2 lbs peaches, peeled and diced
2 cups cider vinegar
1-1/4 cups light brown sugar
1/2 cup raisins
1/2 cup currants

1/2 cup crystallized ginger, chopped
1/2 cup blanched and slivered almonds
2 t each cinnamon, allspice,
   ginger , mustard seed,
   clove, and turmeric

Simmer all ingredients until translucent. If syrup is thin, remove solids and boil to thicken. Spoon into sterilized jars and seal.

Peppered Steak a la Mike Fritzel

At a meeting of the American Physical Society in Chicago, IL, CHAOS
had the pleasure of dining in a lovely old restaurant where
Mike parted with these directions.

Serves 6

INGREDIENTS

1-3/4 lb beef tenderloin	*1 t salt*
2 T virgin olive oil	*1 T crushed black*
1 large sweet onion, diced	*pepper corns*
1 green pepper, diced	*1 oz maggi seasoning*
1 lb fresh mushrooms	*3 dozen small new red potatoes*
2 cloves garlic, minced	*2 oz dry sherry*

1. Sauté the onions and the green pepper, add mushrooms and garlic and continue to sauté until well done.

2. Cut the beef into squares about 1/4 inch thick and sauté them in a separate skillet until they are nicely browned. This can be done in a minimum of olive oil with just a tiny bit of salt free butter added.

3. Now add the meat to the vegetables and add the seasonings plus 2 ounces of dry sherry. Blend everything together and simmer for a few minutes. Empty into a chafing dish and top with well browned little potatoes

Plum Upside Down Cake

Clifford Johnson, University of Kentucky

Serves 6

INGREDIENTS

12 T unsalted butter
1 cup packed golden brown sugar
1 T honey
5 large ripe black plums, cut in half
1-1/2 cups all purpose flour
2 T baking powder
1 t cinnamon

1/4 t salt
1 cup white sugar
2 large eggs
1 T vanilla extract
1/2 t almond extract
1/2 cup milk

1. Preheat oven to 350° Fahrenheit. Melt 6 tablespoons butter and honey over low heat until they mix to form a smooth sauce. Pour into a 9 inch square glass dish. Arrange plum halves in a 3 x 3 square on top of the warm sauce.

2. Cream together the butter and white sugar, add the eggs and beat until light and creamy. Beat in the extracts. Add dry ingredients alternately with the milk. Mix until just blended. Spoon batter over plums.

3. Bake until golden brown and tester inserted comes out clean, about 1 hour. Cool for 20 minutes. Cut around pan sides with a blunt knife to loosen cake. Invert cake onto a plate and let stand for 5 minutes. Lift off pan. Serve with whipped cream.

Portobello Mushroom Marinade

Here's how to marinate and grill those large portobello mushrooms
so they taste like the finest, most tender cut of beef.
From the Symmetry Collection.

INGREDIENTS

6-8 portobello mushrooms
1/2 cup virgin olive oil
1-1/2 cups soy sauce

2 T Dijon mustard (Maille)
1/2 t pepper
fresh juice of 1 lemon

1. Mix together well in a glass baking dish. Remove and keep the stems of the mushrooms for future use. Place the mushrooms in the marinade for 15-30 minutes, turning them over now and then.

2. Place them on a hot grill but not on direct flame. Turn them over now and then. Cook for about 10 minutes or until they become slightly softer and just barely begin to shrink. Serve as disks or cut into 1/4 inch slices.

Pupusa

This recipe was given to Symmetry by Maria Marlene Boñilla, Aspen, CO

Serves 6

INGREDIENTS

2 pounds fried ground pork
5 tomatoes
2 bell peppers
1 red onion

4 cloves garlic
2 pounds mozzarella cheese
Corn Masa Mix
Water

1. Mix in blender the tomatoes, peppers, onion, garlic, cooked pork with 1/2 cup water. Set aside.

2. Combine Corn Masa Mix and water together until consistency is good enough and dry enough to work with to make tortillas.

3. Flatten out tortilla mix to desired size.

4. Mix cheese and meat mix together. (You may use just cheese if you prefer)

5. Add a spoonful of the meat, cheese mix to the center of the tortilla and form into a ball so that the tortilla completely covers the mix.

6. Flatten out the ball to a pancake shape.

7. Repeat until all ingredients are used.

8. Preheat a lightly greased skillet to 350° Fahrenheit, cook lightly oiled papoosas 1 or 2 minutes on each side until cooked.

9. Top with shredded cabbage and enjoy!

Rack of Spring Lamb with Herb Rub, Lamb Stock and Balsamic Reduction

Contributed and tasted by Chris Hyder, Executive Chef,
Elktrout Lodge, Kremmling, Colorado

Herb Rub for the Lamb Racks

Serves 4

INGREDIENTS

1-2 Lamb Racks (Use 1/2 rack per person)
1/4-1/2 cup Herbs de provence
1/4 cup fresh mint (chopped)
Juice of 1 lemon

1-2 T garlic (minced)
Kosher salt (to taste)
Cracked black pepper (to taste)
Olive Oil

1. Trim the lamb racks of most of the fat and any bones that are unnecessary (some bones on the ends), save all trimmings. If you like thick chops take out every other bone, but remember to adjust your portions.

2. Mix everything together, adjust it to your own taste and add enough olive oil to make a thick paste-like consistency.

3. Rub on the trimmed lamb racks and let sit at least 1 hour before cooking.

4. When ready to cook the lamb, grill the racks for about 10-15 minutes for medium rare to medium.

Note: Now make a lamb stock, unless you decide to make the Balsamic Reduction instead (recipes follow).

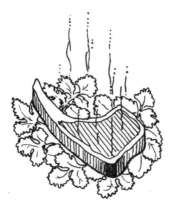

Lamb Stock

INGREDIENTS

Trimming from Lamb racks
1/2 cup each: onion, carrot, celery,
  tomato
4 cloves of garlic (smashed with a pan
 or something)

2 bay leaves
1 T whole black peppercorns
2-3 whole cloves

1. Put all of the above ingredients in a stock pot and cover with water about 2 inches above the trimmings, etc.

2. Bring to boil, skim off the foam and reduce to a simmer. Cook slowly until flavorful and reduced by about one-half.

3. Strain the stock into a sauce pan and bring to a boil. Thicken slightly with a cornstarch and water mixture. Adjust seasoning.

Note: Chris likes to add some fresh rosemary, maybe more garlic.

Balsamic Reduction

This Balsamic Reduction recipe is a delicious and easy sauce to make.
Especially if you don't have the time or desire to make stock.

INGREDIENTS

2 cups Balsamic Vinegar
About 1/2 stick of butter

1. In a saucepan simmer the Balsamic vinegar until reduced by at least one-half.

2. At this time you can thicken the Balsamic with a little cornstarch and water mixture, so it has a syrup-like consistency.

3. Just before serving remove from the heat and whisk in the butter a little at a time, season if necessary.

Note: This is a very bold sauce - you only need a drizzle on each plate.

Red Pepper Soup

Andrea Stryer, tasted by Lubert Stryer, Stanford University

Serves 6

INGREDIENTS

6 peppers
1 cup chopped onions
1 cup chopped leek

2 large potatoes, sliced
1/4 cup olive oil
6 cups chicken broth

1. Char peppers under broiler about 5-8 minutes on each side. Immediately place in a bag and close, allowing peppers to steam for 10 minutes. Peel skins and seed peppers. Set aside.

2. Sauté onions, leek and potatoes slowly in oil until soft, 10-15 minutes. Add the chicken broth and the skinned peppers. Simmer 30 minutes. In batches, puree in food processor. Return to pot and heat. Serve with a sprinkle of chopped chives or parsley.

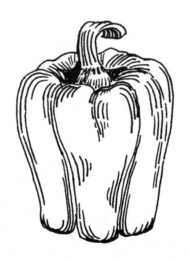

Rich Hazlenut Chocolate Cake

Rena Madansky tasted by Leon Madansky of
Johns Hopkins University

Makes 10 servings
INGREDIENTS

1 cup sweet butter
8 oz bittersweet chocolate
8 eggs, separated

1-1/4 cup sugar
3/4 cup ground hazelnuts
1 T hazelnut liqueur

1. Preheat oven to 325° Fahrenheit. Butter and flour a 10 inch springform.

2. Place butter and chocolate over barely simmering water until melted. Whisk egg yolks with 3/4 cup sugar. Whisk in chocolate, nuts, and liqueur. Whisk egg whites until soft peaks form. Add remaining sugar and whip to form peaks.

3. Stir in 1/3 of whites into chocolate and FOLD in the rest of the egg whites. Scrape batter into pan and bake for 55 minutes. Let cool. The cake will fall. Sift confectioners sugar over the top.

Note: You can fill the fallen cake with whipped cream, flavored with anything you like.

Roasted Rack of Lamb with Raspberry Sauce

Karen Munroe, Basalt, CO, as tasted by Michael Munroe,
Videographer for Aspen Center for Physics

Serves 4

INGREDIENTS

1– 8 rib rack of lamb **or**
  1-saddle/whole loin of lamb
1 head garlic
3 T sugar
1/2 cup raspberry vinegar, divided

1/2 cup water
3 T cold butter
1 t fresh ground pepper
1 pint fresh raspberries **or**
  1-10 oz package frozen

1. Roast lamb at 500° Fahrenheit in a shallow pan on rack for 20 minutes to an internal temperature of 125° Fahrenheit.

2. Remove from oven and cover to rest for a minimum of 5 minutes.

3. Slice chops/loin into medallions and arrange on hot serving platter.

4. Smother in sauce (prepared at the same time).

5. In a sauce pan, mix water, sugar and 1/4 cup vinegar. As it comes to a high simmer, add garlic and cover. Cook until garlic is tender, about 15 minutes.

6. Uncover, lower heat to medium, simmer and cook stirring occasionally until liquid reduces to syrup and garlic begins to caramelize. If needed, hold sauce off of heat until lamb is out of the oven to rest (Step 2).

7. Add remaining vinegar to syrup and any pan drippings and juices from lamb, bring to boil then reduce heat to medium-low.

8. Add butter in three slices, pepper and stir well. Slice meat (Step 3).

9. Add raspberries, quickly and gently fold in berries to coat.

10. Spoon sauce over cut and prepared lamb, serve hot with oven roasted potatoes.

Note: To coordinate preparation, have lamb ready to roast and oven preheated to 500° Fahrenheit (Step 1). Begin sauce (Step 5) and put roast in oven. Proceed with sauce (Step 7) while the Lamb rests. Add raspberries (Step 9) after roast has been cut.

Rocky Mountain Oysters (AKA Balls with Sheep Dip)

Deb Pease, tasted by Jon Pease, Aspen Center for Physics

INGREDIENTS

3 fresh sheep
"oysters"
Marinade:
  oil
  lemon juice
  parsley
  salt and pepper
Batter:
  1 cup all purpose flour

1/2 t paprika
1/4 t salt
1/8 t fresh ground pepper
3/4 cup beer
parsley for garnish
Sauces for dipping:
  tomato, ranch, spicy hot sauce or
  "sheep dip" (ranch doused with
  Tabasco)

1. Order from butcher fresh sheep "oysters".

2. Scald, skin and soak the oysters in cold water for 2 to 3 hours.

3. Combine marinade ingredients, cut the oysters into broad, thin slices and marinate for 1 hour in oil, lemon juice, chopped parsley, salt and pepper.

4. Combine beer batter ingredients, beat until smooth and set aside.

5. Fill deep-fry kettle to a depth of 1-1/2 to 2 inches with cooking oil. Heat oil to 350° to 375° Fahrenheit.

6. Drain oysters, shake lightly with flour, dip into beer batter and fry until golden brown (approximately 10 minutes)

7. Garnish with fried parsley and serve with favorite dipping sauces.

Shrimp and Pink Scallops in the Style of Jalisco

Another Symmetry recipe for a very simple meal.

Serves 6

INGREDIENTS

1/2 t salt
1 cup chopped onion
2 crushed garlic cloves
2 T olive oil
1 28 oz can crushed tomatoes

1/2 cup drained green olives stuffed
   with pimentos
1/4 cup diced green chilies
2 T rinsed capers
1-1/2 lb scallops
1-1/2 lb raw shrimp

1. Sauté onion and garlic but do not brown. Stir in tomatoes, olives, chilies, capers and salt. Heat to boiling, reduce heat and simmer about 15 minutes. Add shrimp and scallops and cook just long enough to cook seafood. Do not overcook! Serve over rice.

Shrimp With Salsa

Virgil Barnes, Purdue University

Serves 4

INGREDIENTS

1 lb peeled raw shrimp (or you can use
   cooked shrimp and throw them in
   at the last minute to heat)
1 red bell pepper cut in strips
1/2 green bell pepper cut in strips
4 cloves garlic, minced
2 medium onions cut in half inch
   squares

2 T olive oil
salt and pepper
1/2 t Tabasco sauce
3 T chopped fresh cilantro
1/2 jar of your favorite Mexican salsa
water equal to the amount of salsa
2 T butter

1. Heat olive oil in a large pan. Stir fry onions and garlic until they are starting to become tender. Add pepper strips and cook until tender-crisp, about 5 minutes.

2. Add butter to the pan and melt. Add shrimp, then salsa, water, salt and pepper, Tabasco and cilantro. Cook just until shrimp are entirely pink and liquid is hot. Serve with rice and salad.

Southwestern Bean Soup

A trip to Santa Fe added this simple soup by Symmetry

Serves 6

INGREDIENTS

1 lb dried beans, any kind, or a mixture
   of the following:
black eyed peas
split green peas
butter beans
pinto beans
red beans
navy beans
great northern beans
small lima beans

pearl barley
lentils
1 large onion, chopped
1 28 oz can tomatoes, chopped
1 T chili powder
1 lemon. Juice only
salt and ground pepper

2 quarts water
1 lb ham hocks

1. Wash beans, cover with fresh water and soak overnight. Drain beans and cover with 2 quarts fresh water and ham hocks, bring to a boil and simmer for 2-1/2 hours.

2. Add: *chopped onion; tomatoes, chopped; chili powder; lemon juice; salt and freshly ground pepper to taste.* Simmer an additional 30 minutes or longer. Serve with a pitcher of medium dry sherry.

Southwestern Marinade for Chicken

Symmetry in Santa Fe

INGREDIENTS

1 T olive oil
2 T lime juice
1/2 cup dry white wine
2 t chili powder
1/4 cup chopped fresh cilantro
salt and freshly ground pepper to taste
(marinate chicken for 10 minutes,
   or up to 1 hour)

Tomatillo Sauce (to serve on marinated chicken):
6 medium tomatillos (husked and
   rinsed)
2 fresh serrano chilies
1-1/2 T olive oil
1/2 medium onion, chopped
1 garlic clove, chopped
1/2 cup chicken broth

Broil chilies and tomatoes. Brown onions and garlic, add chopped chilies and tomatillos and broth. Simmer about 10 minutes.

Spicy Ragout of Ginger Prawns

Suzy Pines, tasted by David Pines, University of Illinois,
and Santa Fe, NM, and Aspen, Colorado

Serves 6

INGREDIENTS

1-1/2 lbs prawns, shelled and deveined, or use high quality large cooked shrimp
2 t coarse salt
2 t cornstarch
1 small egg white
salt
1 T butter
1 T peanut oil
2 T finely chopped shallots
2 T finely chopped scallions
2 T heavy cream

1/2 cup tomato concassé (seeded and cooked ripe tomatoes with a little bit of sugar)
2 t finely chopped fresh hot chilies
2 T finely chopped ginger
1/2 cup finely diced turnips
1/2 cup finely diced carrots
1/2 cup dry white wine
1/4 cup rice wine
1 cup stock
freshly ground white pepper to taste
3 T finely chopped fresh coriander

1. Combine prawns and coarse salt and set aside for 30 minutes. Rinse thoroughly under cold water and dry on paper towels. Combine the cornstarch, egg white, 1 teaspoon salt and prawns in a medium sized bowl and marinate, refrigerated, for 30 minutes.

2. In a wok, heat the butter and peanut oil. Add the shallots, scallions, chilies and ginger and stir fry for 2 minutes. Add the turnips and carrots and stir fry for 2 minutes more. Add the white wine and rice wine and reduce until the cooking liquid is nearly gone. Add the stock and reduce by two-thirds. Add the prawns, cream, tomato concassé, salt and pepper. Cook for 5 minutes, stirring constantly. Add the coriander, stir well, and serve at once.

If using pre-cooked shrimp, dry thoroughly and place in cornstarch mixture as directed; add to sauce, stirring and heating through but being very careful not to overcook.

Note from Suzy: This recipe is a bit of trouble but worth it!

Spicy Remoulade Sauce

Diane Perros, tasted by Dr. Dimitri Perros, Aspen, CO and Winnetka, IL

Serves 10

INGREDIENTS

2 t cayenne pepper
2 t chili powder
2 T capers
2 T chopped parsley
2 T diced onion

2 t salt
2 t white pepper
2 T lemon juice
2 cups good quality mayonnaise,
    bought or home-made

Mix all ingredients and chill for a few hours to blend flavors.

Sweet Potato Casserole

Chaos at Duke University

Serves 6

INGREDIENTS

4 large sweet potatoes, peeled and
    sliced into 1/4 inch rounds
1/4 cup chicken broth
1/4 cup honey
2 t fresh lemon juice

1 t peanut oil
1/2 t salt
1/2 t ground ginger
1/2 t grated nutmeg
1/4 t freshly grated pepper

1. Lightly oil a 2 quart baking dish and layer the sweet potatoes. Combine the remaining ingredients and pour over potatoes. Cover tightly with aluminum foil and bake at 350° Fahrenheit for 1 1/2 hours.

2. Uncover, baste often, and bake until liquid is reduced to a syrup and the top is glazed, another 30-40 minutes.

Turkey Chili

Emolyn Nachtman, Evanston, IL.

Serves 4

INGREDIENTS

2 T olive oil
2 onions, chopped
1 green pepper, chopped
1 can chili pepper, chopped
3 cloves garlic, chopped
2-1/2 cups of chunked, leftover turkey

3 T chili powder
2 T cumin
1 T oregano
1 28 oz can crushed tomatoes
1 square melted unsweetened chocolate
1 can rinsed red beans

1. Combine first six ingredients and sauté until tender and cooked through.

2. Add the remaining ingredients and simmer about 30 minutes to blend flavors.

Tuna

In 1994, the edition of the "New York Times Magazine" section carried a long article written by David Berreby, entitled "Murray Gell-Mann, the Man Who Knows Everything", about Nobelist Gell-Mann, one of the founders and presently an honorary trustee of the Aspen Center for Physics. During the interview, Marcia Southwick, Murray's wife, fixed a tuna fish sandwich.

This tuna fish sandwich prompted a letter to the editor chiding the interviewer for not pointing out that Marcia is a talented poet with a body of work of her own. Marcia replied with a letter to the Times and her recipe for tuna fish sandwiches which Chaos and Symmetry have re-printed here:

"Several people have asked me about my recipe for low-fat tuna fish sandwiches. In our household, making a tuna sandwich means starting from scratch, with quarks.

First, you put a gazillion quarks (and electrons) into a Waring blender-supercollider. Then you mix until life spontaneously generates. After several billion years, a tuna will evolve, by way of natural selection and frozen accidents. The rest is easy."

Marcia Southwick

Unbaked Cream Cheese Pies

CHAOS does not like to prepare desserts, but these pies are an exception.

High caloric and delicious, these fillings are piled into any good, buttery graham cracker crust. Crusts made of butter and crushed chocolate cookies or plain butter cookies are also a possibility. One can incorporate nuts in the crust and a teaspoon of liqueur when applicable.

Walnut – Khalua Filling

INGREDIENTS

16 ounces cold cream cheese
1/2 cup sugar
1/2 cup chopped walnuts
1-1/2 T Khalua liqueur
2 cups whipping cream
1 t vanilla extract
3 T special-blend chocolate, recipe follows

Special Blend Chocolate:
12 ounces semi-sweet chocolate
3/4 cup strong coffee
1 t vanilla or orange extract
1 cup unsalted butter

1. Beat cream cheese in a food processor at high speed for 2 minutes. Add sugar, beat 2 minutes more. Beat in nuts and Khalua. Whip cream with vanilla until stiff and fold into cream cheese. Turn filling into crust, mounding in the center. Drizzle on special blend chocolate and sprinkle on a teaspoon of Khalua. Chill covered, for at least 6 hours before serving.

2. Special Blend Chocolate: in a small saucepan, melt chocolate with coffee, remove from heat and add vanilla. Beat in butter, piece by piece until mixture is smooth. Refrigerate or freeze, makes about 3-1/2 cups.

3. To top Khalua pie, melt Special Blend Chocolate some until it is thin enough to drizzle.

Chocolate Fudge Marble Filling

INGREDIENTS

16 oz cream cheese
1/2 cup sugar
1 cup special blend chocolate, divided

2 cups whipping cream
1 t vanilla extract
1/4 cup slivered almonds

1. Beat cream cheese at high sped for 2 minutes. Add sugar, beat for two minutes. Add 1/2 cup chocolate which should be at room temperature. Beat for 1 minute. Whip cream with vanilla until stiff. Fold into cream cheese mixture. Turn into crust. Cut in remaining 1/2 cup chocolate to make a swirl pattern. Sprinkle with almonds. Chill 6 hours.

Frango™ Mint Filling

INGREDIENTS

6 oz cream cheese
1/2 cup sugar

1 box Frango mints (melted and
    cooled)
2 cups whipping

1. Beat cream cheese 2 minutes, add sugar and beat for 2 minutes. Add cooled Frango mints, beat 1 minute. Whip cream until stiff. Fold into cream cheese mixture. Turn into shell, chill 6 hours.

Grasshopper Cream Cheese

INGREDIENTS

16 oz cream cheese
2/3 cup sugar

20 Grasshopper Chocolate Mint
    Sandwich Cookies, divided
2 cups whipping cream

1. Beat cream cheese at high seed for 2 minutes. Add sugar, beat 2 minutes. Crush about 16 cookies and fold into mixture. Whip cream until stiff. Fold into cream cheese mixture. Turn into crust. Crush remaining cookies and sprinkle over top. Chill for 6 hours.

Wild Rice Salad

Minnesota is the home of wild rice from the Symmetry collection

Serves 8

INGREDIENTS

6 cups cooked wild rice, chilled
1/2 cup chopped red pepper
1/2 cup chopped green pepper
1 bunch green onion, chopped
1/2 cup chopped celery

1/2 cup sliced fresh mushrooms
3 oz slivered and toasted almonds
4 T virgin olive oil
1 T balsamic vinegar
salt and freshly ground pepper

Several hours before serving, combine by gently tossing and chill.

To cook wild rice:

Pour boiling water over 2 cups of wild rice. Let stand at least 1 hour. Drain. Cover with 4 cups of fresh water and 1 teaspoon salt. Bring to a boil and reduce heat to simmer for 40 minutes or until rice has opened and most of the liquid is absorbed. Drain.

World's Best Brownies

Paula Ruderman and agreeing that they are the best, Mal Ruderman, Columbia University

INGREDIENTS

1/2 lb butter
2 cups sugar
4 eggs
1-1/2 cups flour

4 squares melted, unsweetened chocolate
2 cups walnuts, broken pieces
2 t pure vanilla extract

You will need a hand beater and a rectangular baking pan that has been buttered. Cream the butter and sugar and then add the eggs, one at a time, beating after each addition. Add the melted chocolate and the vanilla and then add the flour and the walnuts. Bake at 350° Fahrenheit until done. Cut into squares and dust with powdered sugar.

Zucchini Frittata: A Quiche

Paula Ruderman, tasted by Mal Ruderman, Columbia University

Serves 8

INGREDIENTS

6 eggs well beaten
1 small onion or shallot, grated
1/2 cup oil
2 cups or 3/4 lb Monterey Jack or
*   Sharp Cheddar Cheese*
1 cup Bisquick

6 small to medium zucchini or summer
*   squash or*
2 lbs mushrooms, chopped or
1 lbs mushrooms, domestic and
1 lb wild mushrooms
salt and pepper to taste

1. Add onion to beaten egg, along with the oil, cheese, Bisquick and mushrooms or zucchini.

2. Mix whole mess and put into a pan. Sprinkle top with Parmesan or Romano grated cheese.

3. Bake at 350° Fahrenheit until a knife comes out clean, about 45-60 minutes.

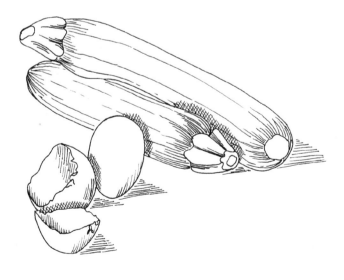

Chaos and Symmetry
present recipes from

ASIA AND THE PACIFIC RIM:

China, India, Indonesia, Japan, Korea and Vietnam

SS. BURRUS

Almond Float

Contributed by Corinne Tan, tasted by Chung-I Tan, Brown University

INGREDIENTS

1 package unflavored gelatin
1 T almond extract
1 cup milk
3/4 cup boiling water
1/3 cup sugar
1/3 cup cold water

Syrup:
2 cups cold water
1/2 teaspoon almond extract
1/3 cup sugar

1. Soften gelatin in cold water and add boiling water and sugar. Stir until thoroughly dissolved. Pour in the milk and the almond extract. Mix well. Pour into oblong 9 x 13 inch cake pan and chill until set.

2. Mix syrup ingredients and chill.

3. Cut gelatin mixture into 1 inch cubes. Serve with mandarin oranges, pineapple chunks and lichee. Ladle 1/2 cup of syrup over each serving.

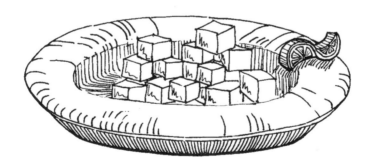

Beef Hekka

Contributed by Corinne Tan, tasted by Chung-I Tan, Brown University
This recipe comes from the former executive chef at the
Royal Hawaiian and Princess Kaiulani Hotels.

Serves 6
INGREDIENTS

1-1/2 lb beef sliced thin
1 cup bamboo shoots, sliced
1 cup mushrooms, sliced
1 bunch green onions, sliced
1/2 bunch water cress, cut in 2" slices
1 medium yellow onion, sliced thin
1 cup celery, sliced

2 branches broccoli, sliced
2 cups shitake mushrooms 2" lengths

Mix together:
2 T salad oil
2/3 cup shoyu
1/3 cup sugar
2 T mirin

1. Heat skillet or wok on high heat. Add salad oil, sauté beef. Season with shoyu mixture. Push beef aside (to corner of pan).

2. Add vegetables to pan and cook quickly. Season with mirin.

3. Stir in mushrooms last, and mix all ingredients together for a few minutes and serve immediately with rice.

Note: Tofu cut into 2" cubes can also be added. Hekka is the Hawaiian version of Sukiyaki. All ingredients should be of equal size and shape.

Chinese Barbecued Pork

On a trip to China, CHAOS learned how to prepare some simple dishes.
This is a favorite.

Serves 4-6

INGREDIENTS

2 lb boneless pork, center cut or
    tenderloin, cut into strips about 5"
    long, 2" wide and 2"thick

Marinade:
4 T chicken stock
3 T soy sauce
1 1/2 T brown bean sauce
2 T sugar
1 T dry sherry
1 t salt
1 t finely chopped garlic
2 to 3 drops red food coloring

1. Mix marinade and immerse pork strips in this mixture and refrigerate for 3 hours. A tightly sealed plastic bag is convenient for this purpose.

2. Remove lower rack from your oven and place one rack in the highest position. Place a roasting pan containing 1 inch of water on the bottom of the oven and preheat to 350° Fahrenheit.

3. Make "S" shaped hooks. These could be made of wire coat hangers, poultry lacers or, in a pinch, heavy weight paper clips. Insert one end of each hook into the top of each pork strip and hang the hooks from the top rack making certain all meat is positioned over the pan of water.

4. Roast pork for 40 minutes, increase temperature to 450° Fahrenheit and roast another 10 minutes. Remove meat from oven and cool. Slice crosswise and serve either hot or cold as part of a Chinese meal.

Note: When serving the pork include 2 dishes of the following sauces for dipping

1. Plum Sauce - this can be made by mixing plum jam and vinegar.

2. English mustard mixed with a bit of water.

Chinese Hot and Sour Soup

Traveling in China gave CHAOS an opportunity to collect many recipes.

Serves 4
INGREDIENTS

4 dried black mushrooms
4 cups chicken stock
1 cup chicken, cut in strips
1/2 cup bamboo shoots,
   cut in julienne strips
1 T soy sauce
1/2 t sugar

2 T cornstarch mixed with
   3 T water
3 T vinegar
1/2 t ground red pepper
1 egg, beaten
2 scallions, chopped

1. Soak mushrooms in hot water for about 15 minutes, drain and slice, removing and discarding the tough stems. Set aside.

2. Bring chicken stock to a boil; when boiling, add chicken, bamboo shoots and sliced mushrooms.

3. Mix soy sauce, sugar and cornstarch and add to soup. Add vinegar and pepper. When soup comes back to a boil, remove from heat and slowly swirl in the egg. Pour soup into bowls and add scallions.

Chinese Salads

This recipe was given to CHAOS by a visitor.
Most vegetables are either parboiled or, at least, rinsed with boiling water.
Be certain to chill the vegetables with cold water before proceeding with the salad,
and then chill the salad in the refrigerator before serving.

INGREDIENTS

Basic dressing:
2 T soy sauce
1 T vinegar
1 t sesame oil
1 t sugar
1 t orange or lemon rind, grated

Vegetables:
asparagus
spinach
cucumber
celery
bean sprouts
ham (cut into strips)
shrimp

1. The dressing can be used on the above fresh vegetables, or a combination of vegetables, meat, chicken, or shrimp.

2. For the spinach, add 1 teaspoon of peanut butter softened in a teaspoon of sesame oil.

Fried Eggplant with Sweet Miso and Sesame Seeds

Contributed by Symmetry

INGREDIENTS

1 eggplant
vegetable oil for frying
1 T Miso
3 T sake

1-2 T sugar
soy sauce
roasted esame seeds

1. Cut eggplant into 4 pieces vertically, then slice lengthwise into 1 centimeter thickness. Soak in cold water for a while and then drain.

2. Add a few tablespoons oil to frying pan and fry eggplant over high heat until transparent.

3. Lower the heat, sprinkle sugar and 2 tablespoons sake over eggplant and toss carefully.

4. Mix Miso, 1 tablespoon sake, and soy sauce. Add to eggplant in pan and toss well.

5. Sprinkle sesame seeds over eggplant and serve.

Golden Grilled Chicken

Contributed by Junko Matsuda, tasted by Satoshi Matsuda, Kyoto University, Kyoto, Japan

INGREDIENTS

2 boneless chicken thighs
ajinomoto (MSG)
4 T Sake
salt
flour
1 egg

2 green onions
2-3 T vinegar
1 t sugar
oil for frying
1 t sesame oil
dash of soy sauce

1. Make thin checkerboard cuts on the surface of the chicken muscle. Mix together the salt, 1 tablespoon sake, MSG, and rub into the chicken surface. Marinate for 10 minutes.

2. Roll chicken in flour, then dip in beaten egg. Add oil to the frying pan and sauté the chicken over high heat till done well.

3. Cut green onions in 3 centimeter lengths. Combine remaining sake, vinegar, sugar, salt, soy sauce and MSG.

4. Remove the chicken from the pan, wipe out the excess oil and return the chicken to the pan. Add the green onion and the sake mixture over the grilled chicken. Cook for 2 minutes over very low heat. Then, sprinkle the sesame oil over all.

5. Cut into slices and serve.

Indonesian Chicken with Soy Sauce

Contributed by Helen Johnson, National Lewis University and Jakarta, Indonesia

Serves 4
INGREDIENTS

3 lb chicken or a medium sized fryer
2 t dark soy sauce
2 shallots, peeled and finely sliced
2 cloves garlic, peeled and crushed
1/2 t chili powder

1/2 lemon or lime, juice only
2 t sesame oil
oil for basting
salt

1. Gently rub the outside of the chicken with salt. Roast at 375° Fahrenheit for 45 minutes or until chicken is golden brown all over. Allow to cool. Divide the chicken into 4 pieces. Use a mallet to beat the chicken flesh and loosen the fibers.

2. Mix together the remaining ingredients to form a marinade for the cooked chicken. Allow the chicken to marinate for 1 hour, turning the pieces from time to time. When ready to serve, place the chicken under the broiler. Brush each piece with oil and broil just long enough to warm through.

Note: Indonesian chickens are road runners and are tough. American chickens are schmoos and tender ones at that.

Indonesian Fried Rice (Nasi Goreng)

Contributed by Helen Johnson, National Lewis University and Jakarta, Indonesia

Serves 8
INGREDIENTS

1 chicken (previously stewed)
1 lb cooked shrimp
1/2 lb cooked crab meat
1/2 lb cooked ham, cut into strips
4 cups broth from the chicken
pinch of salt
3 cups long grain rice
6 T oil
4 medium onions, peeled and chopped

1 red pepper pod, seeded and cut
*   into strips*
2 T oil
3 eggs
1 t Sambal Ulek which is:
*   white pepper, curry, ground ginger,*
*   ground caraway, coriander, ground*
*   nutmeg and saffron*
Parsley for garnish

1. Skin chicken and loosen from bones. Cut into small pieces and set aside. Place 4 cups of broth from the chicken into a pot. Place rice into the boiling broth and reduce the heat. Simmer for 12 minutes, and drain and set aside.

2. Heat 6 tablespoons oil in a large pot. Cook onions, garlic and pepper pod for 5 minutes. Add the rice and steam for 10 minutes, stirring often. Mix shrimp, crab meat, ham and chicken into rice and stir to mix well.

3. Heat 2 tablespoons oil in a skillet. Whisk eggs until frothy and then scramble until firm. Mix your choice of spices with 1 tablespoon water in a cup. Add this to the rice along with the scrambled eggs. Allow to blend for 10 minutes. Dish rice mixture onto a platter, garnish with parsley and serve with your choice of side dishes.

Note: Side dishes, such as spiced pickles, fried banana slices, soy sauce, relishes and roasted peanuts, can be served in bowls on the table for each person to dip into as he or she prefers.

Indonesian Green Beans

Both of these Indonesian dishes are contributed by
Helen Johnson, National Lewis University & Jakarta, Indonesia

Serves 6
INGREDIENTS

1/2 cup onion, chopped
1 clove garlic, minced
2 T lemon rind
1/2 t dried chili peppers
4 T peanut oil

1 lb green beans, preferably fresh,
* or if frozen, thaw first*
1 t salt
pinch of sugar
1 laurel leaf

1. Finely chop onions; add garlic, lemon rind and chili peppers. Heat oil; sauté mixture for 3 minutes, stirring constantly. Add beans and seasonings and mix thoroughly. Cover and cook over low heat until barely tender, adding oil if necessary.

Indonesian Peanut Wafers

These crunchy snacks can be served with hors d'oeuvres or with dinner.

Serves 12
INGREDIENTS

1/2 cup rice flour
2 T ground rice
1/2 t ground cumin
1/4 t ground tumeric
3/4 t salt
1 cup coconut milk

1 clove garlic, peeled and very finely
* crushed*
1 small onion, peeled and very finely
* crushed*
1/4 lb roasted, unsalted peanuts
oil for frying

1. Combine flour, ground rice and seasonings in a small bowl. Stir in the coconut milk and beat until the batter is very smooth. Stir in garlic, onion and peanuts and continue to stir until all the spices are evenly spread throughout the batter.

2. Heat about 1/2 inch of oil in a skillet. Drop the batter by tablespoons into the oil. Each spoonful should spread into a lacy wafer as it cooks. If it is too thick, add another spoonful of coconut milk and stir well. Fry the wafers until golden brown on both sides, turning once. Cool wafers on paper towels over a wire rack to allow air to come through them. Store in an air tight container.

Indonesian Skewered Chicken

Both of these Indonesian dishes are contributed by Helen Johnson
of National Lewis University and Jakarta, Indonesia

Serves 6
INGREDIENTS

4 WHOLE CHICKEN BREASTS

Marinade:
1/2 cup walnuts, chopped
1 lemon, juice only
1 cup hot chicken broth
1 t salt

generous dash of white pepper
1 onion, peeled and diced
1 clove garlic, peeled and crushed
2 T oil

1/2 cup cream and parsley for serving
and garnish

1. Skin and bone the chicken. Cut meat into 1/2 to 1 inch wide strips. Prepare the marinade by mixing walnuts, lemon juice, chicken broth, salt and pepper in a bowl. Add onion, garlic and oil to the mixture. Set aside 1/3 of the marinade for later use.

2. Place chicken strips in marinade and allow to sit for at least 3 hours. Drain chicken and place meat on 4 skewers. Put skewers on a flat pan and cook in a broiler for 20 minutes, turning once. Mix reserved marinade with cream and serve separately. Remove skewers from chicken and put on preheated platter. Garnish with parsley and serve hot.

Indonesian Spiced Cabbage in Coconut Milk

Serves 6
INGREDIENTS

1 lb cabbage, coarsely shredded
2 onions, peeled and chopped
2 fresh red chilies, seeded and chopped
*   or 1 t chili powder*
1 t dried shrimp paste (trasi)
1 daun salam or 3 curry leaves

2 T peanut oil
2 strips lemon rind
1 1/2 cups thick coconut milk
1 t salt
3 T tamarind liquid

1. After shredding the cabbage, blend the onions, garlic and chilies into a fine paste. Use either an electric blender, food processor or mortar and pestle. Wrap the dried shrimp paste in foil and broil for 5 minutes, turning once.

2. In a large saucepan or wok, fry the curry leaves in hot oil for 1 minute. Add the onion paste mixture and the dried shrimp paste and stir fry until the mixture darkens in color.

3. Add lemon rind, coconut milk and salt and reduce heat to simmer. At this point, put in the cabbage and simmer uncovered for about 3 minutes or until cabbage is cooked but still crisp. Last, stir in the tamarind liquid and serve.

Korean Cucumber Salad

Contributed by Lani J. and tasted by Jason Ho, Ohio State University

Serves 6

This is a very popular summer side dish. It is very light, spicy (if you add more chili powder, garlic and vinegar) and very refreshing.

INGREDIENTS

1 lb cucumber (pickling, hot house or regular market cucumber), if the seeds are too large, take them out by scraping them with a spoon
1-2 t salt (if you like soy sauce can substitute with it)
1-2 stalks green onion

1-2 cloves garlic, peeled and crushed or chopped fine (you can use garlic powder, which is less pungent)
3-4 t white vinegar
1/2 t sugar
2 t sesame oil

1. Cut the cucumber in julienne style or any kind of thin slices. Salt it first and put it aside for about an hour, then drain the excess liquid. Add all the ingredients together, saving the sesame oil to the very last minute, just before you serve it.

Korean Pan Grilled Chicken

Contributed by Lani J. and Lee Ho and tasted by Jason Ho, Ohio State University

Serves 4

INGREDIENTS

1 lb boned and skinned chicken meat
4 T soy sauce
1-1/2 T sugar
2-3 cloves garlic, peeled and crushed
1 piece of fresh ginger, peeled and grated
3 spring onions, chopped

freshly ground black pepper
2 T sesame oil
2 T rice wine
1 T vegetable oil
4 large mushrooms, cut into 3-4 pieces
4 fresh hot green peppers, cut crossways into 1/2" segments

1. Combine and mix the soy sauce, sugar, garlic, ginger, spring onion, sesame oil, rice wine and pepper in a large bowl. Cut the chicken into thin slices 1/4" thick and mix with the sauce.

2. Just before serving, heat the oil in a non-stick frying pan over very high heat. When hot, put in the chicken slices, laying them out flat in one layer. Cook about 1 minute on each side or until lightly browned.

3. When the chicken is done, put the mushrooms and green peppers into the frying pan and pour the remaining marinade over them. Stir and cook until done. Mix the vegetables and chicken together and serve immediately. you can vary all the ingredients the way you like, just remember to cook the meat at a very high temperature for a short time so that it remains juicy and tender.

Lamb with Yogurt and Tomato

Contributed by Helga Singwi and tasted by Kundan Singwi,
Northwestern University

Serves 6
INGREDIENTS

500 gm boned lamb, cubed
60 ml oil or ghee*
5 large cloves garlic, crushed
4 cm ginger root, finely chopped
4 cloves
4 black pepper corns
2 laurel leaves
2.5 cm cinnamon stick
1 black cardamom pod

10 ml ground coriander
2.5 ml ground red chili
2.6 ml ground turmeric
400 gm canned tomatoes
150 ml plain yogurt
30 ml chopped fresh or dried fenugreek
100 ml water
salt

1. Heat the oil or ghee and fry the garlic, ginger, onion and whole spices until golden. Add the meat and fry until golden, about 10 minutes.

2. Stir in the ground spices, tomatoes and salt and cook for 10 minutes until the liquid has been absorbed and the oil appears on the surface. Add the yogurt and fenugreek and cook for 10 minutes until the liquid has been absorbed. Add the water and cook over low heat for 5 more minutes until the meat is tender.

3. For the garnish, combine 2.5 Garam Masala**, 15 ml chopped fresh coriander and 1 small chopped green chili. Sprinkle over the top of the dish and serve hot. Serve with chapatis, dal, fried bitter gourd or cauliflower, raita and plain rice.

*Ghee is clarified butter and can be bought in Asian grocery stores.
**Garam Masala is a combination of spices and can be bought in an Asian Grocery.

Pacific-Asian Lunch

These recipes come from Corinne Tan, who writes,
"This meal is light and refreshing on a hot summer's day."
It is one of Chung-I's (her husband, who is a professor at Brown University)
favorites and it was a frequent request of his late father.

Serves 4
INGREDIENTS

1 lb flank steak
1 bunch water cress
8-12 oz bean sprouts
1 cucumber
2 eggs
1 pkg Somen noodles

Somen Sauce:
1/4 cup sugar
1 cup chicken broth
1/4 cup shoyu
1/4 t vinegar
2 T sesame oil
   (boil sauce ingredients for
   5 minutes and chill)

Meat Marinade:
1/4 cup shoyu
1/4 cup sesame oil
2 T sugar
1/8 t pepper
1/8 t salt
1 garlic clove, minced
1/4 cup green onions, chopped
1 T sesame seeds, roasted

1. Slice the flank steak into as thin strips as possible and marinate the steak while the rest of the meal is being prepared.

2. Slightly beat the eggs and fry into thin pancakes. Cut into strips and set aside. Wash and cut the watercress into 1 inch lengths. Blanch the watercress and the bean sprouts by pouring boiling water over them in a sieve. Pour 2 tablespoons shoyu, 2 tablespoons sesame oil and 1 tablespoon sesame seeds over the vegetables.

3. Cut the cucumber into 2 inch strips and sauté until slightly cooked. Cook somen noodles according to package directions, drain and chill.

4. Broil meat and slice thinly. Serve over somen noodles. Garnish with the vegetables and egg strips. Serve the somen sauce in another container for guests to ladle on the dish according to their tastes.

Note: Serve with "Almond Float", page 113 for dessert.

Pakora, An Indian Delicacy

Both of these recipes were contributed by K. Wali,
tasted by K.C. Wali, Syracuse University

Serves 4
INGREDIENTS

Basic Batter:
8 oz besan (graham flour)
1/4 t baking powder
1/2 t turmeric
1 t coriander powder
1/2 t chili powder
salt to taste

Vegetables:
8 oz onions
Eggplant cut in 1/4 inch rounds
cauliflower florets
spinach leaves

1. Sieve besan, baking powder, turmeric, coriander, chili and salt into bowl. Gradually add water and beat to a thick batter.

2. To make pakoras, 8 ounces onions may be chopped and added to the batter and dropped in teaspoonfuls into the hot fat or oil and deep fried until crisp. Or the above vegetables can be dipped in the batter and then fried.

Pakora Potato Chips

Serves 4
INGREDIENTS

1 lb potatoes
vegetable fat for frying

1 T besan
salt to taste

1. Peel and slice potatoes as for chips. Sprinkle salt and besan over the potatoes and deep fry.

Pickled Cauliflower

Contributed by Junko Matsuda, tasted by Satoshi Matsuda, Kyoto University

INGREDIENTS

1 head of cauliflower	3/4 cup rice vinegar
1 onion	2 t sugar
ginger	salt

1. Divide the cauliflower into small florets and wash carefully. Cook the florets in boiling salted water for 1 minute. Drain.

2. Thinly slice the onion and ginger and put in a sauce pan. Add rice vinegar, sugar and salt. Cook briefly over low heat.

3. Combine this onion mixture with the cauliflower.

4. Chill well before serving.

Pickled Eggplant

A trip by CHAOS to India produced a thick folder of wonderful things to prepare

INGREDIENTS

small eggplants	1/2 cup vegetable oil per liter container
pickling salt	pressed garlic
cider vinegar	crushed oregano
1/2 cup olive oil per liter container	crushed hot pepper

1. Pare and slice the eggplant thinly, no more than 1/4 inch thick. Salt each slice on both sides. Spread on paper towels and cover with a heavy weight overnight.

2. Boil enough cider vinegar to cover the slices. Put them into the boiling vinegar for 1 minute only. Remove slices and squeeze out excess vinegar between towels.

3. Make a mixture, about 1 cup per sterilized quart jar, of the two oils. Pour a little oil into the jar, put in a slice of eggplant, sprinkle with garlic and spices and cover with a little more oil. Continue to alternate slices and spices and oil until the jar is full. Cover the jar and let stand for at least a month before eating. Do not refrigerate as this will harden the oil.

Note: This recipe seems to last indefinitely if you can keep your hands off the slices! Great as an hors d'oeuvre.

Pickled Sweet Japanese Cabbage

Contributed by Junko Matsuda, tasted by Satoshi Matsuda, Kyoto University

INGREDIENTS

400 gm Nappa Cabbage
2 dried red peppers
vegetable oil
2 T sugar

3 T rice vinegar
salt
ajinomota (MSG)

1. Cut white parts of Nappa into 5 centimeter length and 5 millimeter width.

2. Remove the seeds from the red peppers

3. Heat oil in frying pan over high heat, add Nappa and chopped pepper and fry quickly.

4. Add sugar, rice vinegar, salt and ajinomoto and toss to coat.

5. Chill well before serving.

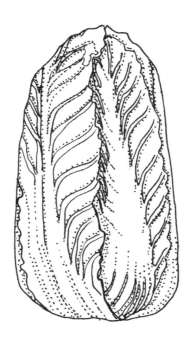

Roast Beijing Duck
with Wonderful Crispy Skin

CHAOS does not make the pancakes for this dish.
Some steamed rolls will work very well.

Serves 6
INGREDIENTS

1 duck
1 t salt
1/2 t freshly ground pepper
3 cloves garlic
3 large slices of fresh ginger

1/4 cup honey
2 scallions cut into 1" length
5 cups water
Boil the preceding 4 ingredients for
   a few minutes and discard

1. *First Day*: Make certain that the duck is thoroughly thawed, remove as much fat as you can and then pour 5 cups of boiling water over the skin.

2. When cooled, sprinkle the duck with salt and pepper on both the inside and the outside and place it on a V-shaped rack in a roasting pan. NOW REFRIGERATE THE DUCK UNCOVERED FOR 24 HOURS.

3. *Second Day:* Preheat the oven to 450° Fahrenheit. Put garlic and ginger in the cavity and prick the skin all over. For the next 45 minutes pour about 1/4 cup boiling water over the duck every 15 minutes. The duck should be in the oven for 45 minutes, therefore, deduct the time it takes to bathe it. When done, the juices should run clear with just a tinge of pink. Let cool 15 minutes before carving and serving.

Samosas
A Specialty of India

All of the Samoas recipes were contributed by
Kanwal Yodh, tasted by Gorang Yodh, University of California

Serves 4

INGREDIENTS

Pastry:
1 lb plain flour
1/2 t baking powder
1 t salt
1 ounce melted butter or ghee
4 T yogurt

Filling:
2 ounces ghee or butter
1 small onion
1 lb boiled potatoes
2 green chilies
salt to taste
1 t garam masala
vegetable fat for deep frying

1. To make the pastry, sieve the flour, baking powder and salt into a bowl. Add the melted butter or ghee and the yogurt and make into a pliable dough. Knead thoroughly so that the dough is smooth.

2. To make filing, heat the two ounces ghee and fry the chopped onion for 2 minutes. Add the potatoes and chilies cut into small pieces and fry for 5 minutes. Add salt and garam masala and mix thoroughly. Take off the fire and cool.

3. Knead dough again. Take small walnut size pieces of the dough and make into round balls. Flatten and roll out on a floured board. Make thin rounds the size of a saucer. Cut in half. Make into a cone, seal with water and fill with the potato mixture. Wet open edges with water and press together. When all the Samosas are ready, fry in deep fat till they are crisp and golden.

Samosas with Meat

INGREDIENTS

Pastry: _Same as plain Samosas_

Filling:
1 onion
2 cloves garlic
1 oz ghee or butter

12 oz minced meat
2 t coriander
1/2 t ginger
1/2 t chili
1 t garam masala
salt to taste

1. Chop the onion and garlic into very small bits. Heat the ghee and fry the onion and garlic till golden. Add the meat, spices and salt and fry for 5 minutes. Cover and cook over gentle heat until the meat is cooked. Cool and make the Samosas.

2. Assemble the same as plain Samosas.

Samosas with Potatoes and Peas

INGREDIENTS

Pastry: _Same as plain Samosas_

Filling:
1 onion
2 oz ghee or butter

8 oz boiled diced potatoes
8 oz peas
2 green chilies, chopped
salt to taste
1 t garam masala

1. Fry the chopped onion in the ghee for 2 minutes. Add the potatoes, peas and chilies and fry for 5 minutes. Add the salt and the garam masala. Take off the fire and cool. Make into Samosas with the pastry in the preceding recipes.

Sushi Rolls

The following Sushi recipes came to us from Korean born Jackie Nielson who now resides in Colorado. Each family has their own distinctive recipe variations which come from their very soul and are handed down, generation to generation. Sushi is actually a Japanese word which signifies that the main ingredient in a recipe is vinegared rice. These recipes for sushi are made with a Korean flavor. Ingredients can be altered to suit personal tastes.

Kimbob (Seaweed Roll)

INGREDIENTS

Thin sliced roast beef, marinated briefly in soy sauce, sesame oil, roasted sesame seeds, crushed garlic & pepper, then cut into strips
1 package of roasted seaweed sheets
2 diakon, Korean pickled yellow radishes, julienned
fresh spinach leaves, blanched, then drained and gently squeezed to remove excess water. Toss with chopped green onions, garlic powder, and soy sauce or salt to season. Lay leaves stretched out on a plate

2 eggs. beaten and then fried like a crepe. Remove from pan and slice thin like noodles.
2 carrots, julienned, sautéed in sesame oil till crisp, tender and seasoned with garlic powder

Rice Mixture:
3 ½ cups cooked rice tossed with 3 T vinegar, 1 T sugar, 1 t salt & roasted sesame seeds

Rolling Instructions for Sushi

1. Beginners might find it useful to have a sushi roller or a piece of waxed paper to aid in the rolling process. Place a piece of roasted seaweed about one inch up from the sushi roller or waxed paper.

2. Spread a good amount of rice over the seaweed, leaving a half inch space at the upper edge.

3. Place prepared ingredients 1½" from the lower edge, and extending the width of the seaweed, building one item upon the next to form layers. (This will give a beautiful flower effect once sushi is rolled and sliced).

4. Pick up the roller from the bottom and roll around the inside ingredients, jelly roll fashion, making sure to get a good tuck so that there are no empty pockets inside the roll.

5. Press the top edge of the roll to seal the seam. Slice the roll into pieces of desired width.

6. Serve the sushi cool or at room temperature and with dipping sauces of soy and wasabi.

California Roll

INGREDIENTS

1 package of roasted seaweed sheets
Rice Mixture:
   3 ½ cups cooked rice tossed with
   3 T vinegar, 1 T sugar, 1 t salt &
     roasted sesame seeds

crab sticks, shredded
toasted sesame seeds,
  sprinkled in a row
avocado, peeled, seeded and julienned
cucumber, peeled and julienned
flying fish roe, sprinkled in a row

1. Use rolling instructions for sushi from previous page.

Philadelphia Roll

Use half a seaweed sheet per roll.
When sliced these make little appetizers

INGREDIENTS

1 package of roasted seaweed sheets,
  cut in half
Rice Mixture:
   3 ½ cups cooked rice tossed with
   3 T vinegar, 1 T sugr, 1 t salt &
     roasted sesame seeds

1 - 8 ounce package of cream cheese cut
    in ¼" strips, thickness can vary
    depending on personal preference
1 bunch of green onions,
    livered lengthwise
smoked salmon, slivered

1. Use rolling instructions for sushi from previous page.

Vietnamese Spring Rolls

Marisa Farland Silverman tasted by Jack Silverman, Aspen, Colorado

INGREDIENTS

1/2 cup shredded carrots
1/2 cup diakon radish
1/4 cup mint
1/4 cup basil
1/4 cup cilantro
1/2 cup green leaf lettuce

1/2 cup sprouts (blend of broccoli,
    clover, mustard)
1/2 cup fresh cooked crab, shrimp or
    tofu
1 pkg rice flour skins
plum sauce
peanut satay sauce

1.   Shred carrots and radish. Chop mint, basil, and cilantro, then mix. Chop shrimp, crab and tofu or whatever combination you prefer.

2.   Soak skins in hot water, 4 at a time, and pat dry on towels when they are pliable.

3.   Arrange 2 skins overlapping, place lettuce (without rib) in center and place a small quantity of everything else on the lettuce. fold in sides. Fold one end over, away from yourself and then roll. Seal with water on edge of skin.

4.   To serve, cut in 1/2 on the diagonal and arrange on a plate, garnish with cilantro, or cut into disks with a wet knife, arrange and garnish. On each plate, place 1 or 2 teaspoons of peanut satay sauce and 1 or 2 teaspoons of sweet and sour plum sauce for dipping.

Chaos and Symmetry
present recipes from
EASTERN EUROPE:

Armenia, Hungary, Lithuania, Poland, Russia and The Czech Republic

SS.BURRUS

Armenian Rice Pilaf

Stephan Isberian, as tasted by Heather Isberian, Aspen, CO

INGREDIENTS

1/2 to 1 stick of butter
1/2 bag of fine egg noodles

2 cups of Long Grain Rice
4-1/2 cups of chicken broth

1. In a heavy pot add butter and melt slowly. Add noodles and stir constantly. Butter will froth up, stir until the noodles turn white. Do not let the butter burn or separate. Add rice and stir quickly to get rice coated with butter.

2. Add chicken broth and bring to a boil. Turn down burner to low (2 on electric). Cover with tight lid. Stir after 10 minutes, simmer for 20 minutes then check if broth is absorbed. Taste when rice is totally cooked remove from heat and keep covered.

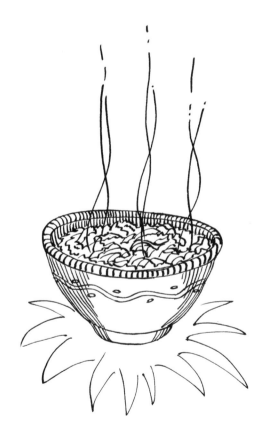

Bigos

Bigos is the standard-bearing dish of the Polish cuisine.
Professor Maria Krawcik, University of Warsaw, Poland

INGREDIENTS

Sauerkraut
Meats:
   ham, leg of lamb, beef, pig's neck
boletus mushrooms
prunes

Spices:
laurel leaves, red pepper, caraway
   seeds, honey
1/2 quart vodka
smoked bacon

Bigos is hard to concoct. It contains a multitude of components. Various spices and dried fruits, also alcohol. The cooking of bigos is enormously time consuming, requiring not only the proper selection of the ingredients but also the need to adhere to a strict chronology when adding them. Reheated many times, bigos gains in its bouquet.

1. Remove the sauerkraut from its oak barrel and rinse it with cold water, so it is not too sour. After chopping raw meat in large pieces, fry it in lard, the more kinds of meat there are, the more refined will the bigos be. It is best to take ham, leg of lamb, beef and pigs neck. When this cut-up mass of meat has only been very lightly braised in the pan and has enclosed all its juices, mix it together with the sauerkraut, pour a small amount of water over it and let it simmer. Add a lot of boletus mushrooms and cover with two handfuls of prunes.

2. Next come spices, add laurel leaves, red pepper and then insert a large amount of caraway seeds and a lesser quantity of honey. Cut up smoked bacon separately in the same way as the meat and as the first stage of cooking approaches, add to the rest of the dish. Always remember that the smoked ham and bacon should never be previously boiled or scalded. Now remove the bigos from the stove and put it in a cool place.

3. The next day cook it once more and towards the end, pour in 1/2 quart vodka, and chill it again.

4. On the third day get the bigos to simmer more strongly and finally add salt, herbs and sugar to taste. It must be remembered that bigos is only good when three tastes can be distinguished - the aroma of the mushrooms, the sourness of the cabbage and the sweetness of the honey.

5. Serve with dark bread and you will find out how magnificent a main course it is.

HUNTER'S BIGOS contains venison.

ROGUE'S BIGOS is prepared in an entirely different way, using all left over bits of roast, smoked meats and gravy which can be found in a household. This is an inferior version of bigos.

Czech Fruit Dumplings

Vendula and Petr Vogel, Cal Tech

INGREDIENTS

3 cups all purpose flour
1 pkg dry yeast
dash salt

1 egg
1-1/4 cup water
fresh fruit with pits

1. Mix flour, yeast, and salt. Add liquids, mix and work with spatula into smooth dough. Let rise for 2 hours.

2. Roll into cylinder. Cut into pieces (about 10 for large fruit such as apricots or about 15 for Italian plums or cherries, 3 cherries per dumpling).

3. Make a circle, put fruit in center, seal up, let rise for 10-15 minutes.

4. Cook in boiling water for 5-10 minutes, depending on size. Serve with cottage cheese, sugar, and burned butter.

Guylas

(Goulash, Gypsy or Szegedine or Szekely)
CHAOS in Budapest
Every Hungarian has his or her own version of this national dish. We have simplified the procedure and now serve at least two kinds at every dinner party.

Serves 8

INGREDIENTS

4 lbs lean beef cut in cubes, or a
    combination of beef and pork
6 large onions
2 T olive oil
2 t caraway seeds
1 t marjoram

2 t salt
6 t Hungarian rose paprika
2 t vinegar
1-1/2 cups red wine
1-2 bullion cubes dissolved in water

1. Sauté the onions in olive oil until tender and golden, add caraway seeds, marjoram, salt and paprika moistened with vinegar and mix well.

2. Add meat and brown nicely and add wine and bullion, cover and simmer for about 2 hours or until meat is tender.

Short cut for Szekely Gulyas (Transylvanian):

1 large can of very good quality sauerkraut.
    (If imported from Germany, it is already mild and cooked in wine. If domestic, wash the kraut well in several changes of water and drain.)
1 medium can of tomatoes, recipe ready, diced in juice.
1 16 oz container of sour cream

1. Take 1/2 of the basic gulyas to be served. In a casserole, layer sauerkraut, tomatoes and gulyas alternating in several layers. Simmer on top of the stove or in the oven for another hour.

2. This can now be served with a bowl of sour cream to be used as topping. Another version is to whisk 1 cup sour cream with 2 tablespoons flour, carefully stir into gulyas and simmer 10 more minutes before serving.

This should all be served with Spaetzle and a nice cucumber salad on the side.

Hungarian Goulash

CHAOS collected this version on a trip to Budapest
It is simple and good.

Serves 6

INGREDIENTS

2 lb boneless lean beef, cut into cubes
3 very large onions, sliced
1 T olive oil
1 t caraway seeds
1/2 t marjoram

1 t (or more) salt
4 t paprika
1 t vinegar
1 cup dry red wine

1. Sauté onions in oil until tender and golden; add caraway seeds, marjoram, salt and paprika moistened with vinegar, mix well.

2. Add meat and brown nicely on all sides.

3. Add wine, cover tightly and simmer very slowly for about 4 hours, or until meat is tender. Add water during cooking if necessary.

Kasha

To CHAOS from a Russian friend

Serves 6

INGREDIENTS

1 cup coarse kasha (buckwheat groats)
1 egg
1 t salt
8 T butter

2-3 cups boiling water
1-1/2 cups chopped onions
3/4 lb fresh chopped mushrooms

1. Mix the lightly beaten egg together with the groats until all grains are coated. Place into large frying pan and cook until all grains are lightly toasted. Add salt, a few tablespoons of the butter and 2 cups of boiling water. Simmer for about 20 minutes. If the kasha is too dry and firm, add another cup of water and simmer for about 10 more minutes until all the water is absorbed and the grains separated and fluffy. Let rest 10 minutes.

2. In another skillet, melt 3 tablespoons butter and sauté the onions and the mushrooms until all liquid has disappeared. Mix this mixture with the kasha. Taste for seasoning.

Lamb Shanks

Stephen Isberian, of Armenia and Aspen, Colorado

INGREDIENTS

6-8 lamb shanks
2 large cans of crushed tomatoes
2 heads garlic, chopped coarsely
2-3 laurel leaves
2 bunches parsley, chopped
2 bunches cilantro, chopped
1 cup olive oil
1 cup red wine
2 t cumin

salt and pepper
2 red or green peppers, cut into
   large pieces
3 large onions, cut into quarters and
   separated
1 dozen mushrooms
several hot peppers, chopped
any other spices you may like
Beef or chicken broth

1. In a large skillet, add olive oil and bring to high heat but not smoking. Season shanks with salt, pepper and garlic. Braise shanks in the olive oil, brown shanks on all aside adding olive oil if necessary. Remove from skillet.

2. Sauté mushrooms, peppers and onions and discard olive oil.

3. Place shanks and vegetables in a large roasting pan. Add all of the ingredients and enough broth to almost cover the shanks. Tightly cover with lid or foil. Bake at 275° Fahrenheit for 6-10 hours, or at 250° Fahrenheit overnight. Every few hours, skim the grease off the top. The shanks are done when the meat falls off the bone. While cooking, try not to damage the shanks by over-stirring the mixture. Serve on a bed of rice, bulgar pilaf or egg noodles.

Lithuanian Borscht

This recipe is a traditional one given to Dr. Patricia C. Boeshaar by her grandmother, tasted many times over the years by her husband, Dr. Tony Tyson, Distinguished Member, Technical Staff, Bell Laboratories, Lucent Technologies, Murray Hill, NJ. The result looks like pink anti-freeze, but tastes like ambrosia!

INGREDIENTS

*1 lb red beets, or
1 15 oz can of red beets, grated
1/2 sweet red or white onion
1 qt milk*

*1/2 cup sour cream
5 T vinegar, white or cider
Salt and pepper to taste*

1.   Mix the above ingredients well in a large bowl.

2.   Thin out the mixture with enough milk (at least 1 qt.) to attain soup consistency, then chill the soup.

Note: All ingredients can be adjusted to taste and yogurt could be substituted, however, the results will not taste the same.

This soup is traditionally eaten with small boiled potatoes served **HOT** and added by each person to their soup, one at a time. A thicker consistency would turn the soup into a dip which could be served as an appetizer with the potatoes.

Mandle Brait

This recipe is from a book by the late Bernice Mink,
submitted by Dr. Barry Mink of Aspen, Colorado

INGREDIENTS

3 cups flour
1 cup sugar
3 eggs
1 cup pecans, chopped
3/4 cup butter

1-1/2 t baking powder
3/4 t salt
3/4 t vanilla
sugar and cinnamon

1. Mix ingredients. Divide into 3 long strips. Sprinkle top with mixture of sugar and cinnamon. Bake for 10 minutes at 350° Fahrenheit.

2. Remove from oven, slice diagonally and return to oven to brown. Watch carefully!

Stuffed Cabbage "A Lot of Bother"

Paula Ruderman obtained this recipe from her Hungarian mother,
tasted by Mal Ruderman, Columbia University

Serves 8

INGREDIENTS

2 lbs ground beef
1 8 lb head of cabbage
1 cup bread crumbs (flavored) in 1/2
   cup or so milk or water
4 eggs
salt and pepper to taste

2 T parboiled rice
2 cans of "concentrated" tomato soup
1 small can tomato sauce
2 large onions
2 T sugar
1 squeeze (big one) of lemon - ugh!

1. Remove core of cabbage. Separate leaves and boil in a large pot of water until flexible. Remove tough spines of leaves with knife. When the leaves get too small to use for wrapping meat, coarsely chop and add to sauce.

2. In one huge or two large pots, heat a little oil and caramelize the onions with the sugar.

3. In a separate large bowl combine beef, eggs, bread crumbs, rice, salt and pepper. Place an appropriate amount on leaf, roll up and tuck in sides.

4. Place all the stuffed leaves in the pots on top of onions. Pour the tomato soup over the cabbage rolls and add the lemon juice and the leftover chopped cabbage. Cover the pot and cook on top of the stove for at least 1 hour. Cool and refrigerate at least one day before serving.

Stuffed Cabbage Leaves

There are many happy eaters from Russia working at CERN in Geneva, Switzerland
CHAOS had no problem learning how to stuff cabbage leaves
and prepare them for a delicious dinner.

Serves 4

INGREDIENTS

1 lb ground round steak	1/2 t paprika
1/2 lb ground lean pork	juice of 1/2 lemon
1 large head of cabbage	1 egg
1 T olive oil	4 T olive oil
1 medium sized onion	1 T flour
1 green pepper	1 cup tomatoes (fresh or canned)
3 stalks celery	1/2 cup dry red wine
1 clove garlic	1 laurel leaf
1 cup cooked rice	3/4 cup sour cream
2 T chopped parsley	salt and pepper to taste

1. Get a large head of cabbage, separate the leaves, and pick out 12 perfect ones. Cut away the hard part at the bottom of each leaf and scald the leaves in salted water for about 8 minutes. This makes them pliable. Spread the leaves out on a towel and let them dry.

2. In a skillet, gently sauté until tender the onion, pepper, celery and garlic (all chopped) in 1 tablespoon of the olive oil.

3. In a large bowl, mix the meats, rice, parsley, the sautéed vegetables, salt and pepper, paprika, lemon juice and egg. Stir the mixture until blended and then divide into 12 portions. Fold each portion in a cabbage leaf, folding the leaf to make a neat package. Tie the packages with thread or use toothpicks.

4. Heat the rest of the olive oil and brown the rolls, remove them and keep them warm. Stir 1 tablespoon of flour into the oil in the pan and blend. Add 1 cup of tomatoes, breaking up any large pieces, and 1/2 cup of the dry red wine. Let this boil up, then add the crumbled laurel leaf and the 3/4 cup sour cream and mix well. Then, after removing the thread or toothpicks, put the rolls back in the pan. Cook them in a moderate oven (350° Fahrenheit) for about 1 hour.

SS.BURRUS

Traditional
Cuisine
of Russia

The following recipes are from the traditional cuisine of Russia which is said to have been developed in the 15th Century and added to in the 18th Century by using ideas from the fine cuisine developed in Western Europe.

We would like to credit "Russian Cookery 2000" for the recipes, published by Copper Horseman Trading House of Saint Petersburg, Russia and The Podvorie restaurant of St. Petersburg where the cooking traditions of olden days have been revived.

These recipes were sent to Chaos by Tatiana Pavlovna Amineva, physicist at Moscow State University, who with her husband, physicist Sergei Slavatinsky also of Moscow State University, attended a meeting of cosmic ray physicists in Lodz, Poland, where Chaos and her husband Martin were in attendance in the winter of 1999.

Chaos and Symmetry would like to credit the calendar "Russian Cookery 2000", for the following recipes, published by Copper Horseman Trading House, 3 Mira Street, Saint Petersburg, Russia 197101 Telephone: (812) 237-0733/Fax: (812) 232-7806.

Blini or Russian Pancakes

Serves 4
INGREDIENTS

1-3/4 cups flour
6-1/2 cups milk
2 eggs

1 T sugar
1/2 t salt
2-3 T vegetable oil

1. Use a mixer to beat the eggs, salt and sugar until well blended, then pour the milk into the batter, stir, then add the vegetable oil and mix well.

2. Grease an iron pan to make the pancakes on. Mix the flour into the dough adding a small amount of vegetable oil, because if you do not add oil with the flour, the foaming capacity of the eggs would decrease and the dough would not have enough air in it to make the pancakes rise.

3. Serve the blini hot with butter, sour cream or jam.

Borscht Moskovskaia

Serves 8
INGREDIENTS

500 gms beef brisket, boiled and
  cubed
beef stock
Ham, 100 gms boiled and cut into
  cubes
2 T butter
2 large onions, chopped
1 kg beets, peeled and cut into strips

1 dl red wine vinegar
1 t sugar
1/2 kg white cabbage coarsely shredded
parsley
1 laurel leaf
100 gms of finely cut dill
salt and pepper to taste

1. Sauté onions in butter until they are soft and golden. Stir in the beets and add the vinegar, sugar, salt and pepper. Add the beef broth and simmer for about 1 hour.

2. Pour the remaining stock into the pot and add the cabbage. Bring to a boil and add the ham and beef. Add the parsley and laurel leaf. Transfer the borsch to a tureen and sprinkle with the fresh dill. Accompany with a bowl of sour cream.

Chopped Cutlets of Elk Meat

36 oz serves 4
INGREDIENTS

Elk Meat, 9 ounces per serving
1/2 cup vinegar
4 laurel leaves

a handful of peppercorns
4 dill pickles
salt and pepper to taste

1. Boil a pot of water, add the vinegar, laurel leaves, peppercorns and pickles and put in the elk meat.

2. Boil the meat for 1 hour or so, depending on the amount you are cooking, then put the meat through a grinder. Make patties out of the ground meat, add some butter and some more salt and pepper and bake them in a moderate oven for 15 minutes.

Fish Okroshka Soup (Cold Kvass Soup)

Serves 2
INGREDIENTS

1-3/4 oz fish (boiled, dried or
  smoked)
10 oz Bread kvass (a kind of beer)
30 oz cucumbers
40 oz spring onions
1 egg, hardboiled
4 oz sour cream

salt
sugar
horseradish
dill
parsley
mustard

1. Cut fish into small slices and the cucumber into narrow strips. Mince the hard boiled egg.

2. Shred and rub spring onions with salt until juicy. Put onions, mustard, salt and sugar into the sour cream and stir well, then pour in the kvass, and add the fish, egg, dill and parsley.

Goose with Apples

Serves 8
INGREDIENTS

1 goose, 10 to 14 pounds
apples, 4 to 6 pounds
raisins, a handful
1 t caraway seeds
1 t marjoram
pinch of salt

fresh greens in season (lettuce, parsley,
   cucumber)
1 cup dry white wine
1 cup honey
1/2 cup sour cream
1/2 cup pomegranate juice
1/2 lb cranberries or cranberry jelly

1. Rub the bird with salt and spices, inside and out. Stuff it with chopped apples and raisins. Sew up the cavity with cooking twine, then sprinkle the bottom of the roasting pan with the cup of wine and rub the outside of the bird with vegetable oil and place it back down in the roasting pan.

2. Cover the pan and set the oven at 375° to 400° Fahrenheit and put the bird in to cook, checking it after 15 minutes to 1/2 hour to see if there is enough fat to begin a gravy. If the goose seems dry, mix the honey, sour cream and pomegranate juice and pour the mixture over the bird, cover it and put it back in the oven to finish cooking. Depending on its size, the goose will need to cook between 2 and 3 hours.

Honey Hearts

Honey cakes are given at New Years as a wish of quietude and wealth and they are also used to decorate Christmas trees.

INGREDIENTS

5-1/2 ounces honey
1-3/4 ounces butter
14 ounces wheat flour
1/2 t baking soda
1/2 t cinnamon

1/2 t anise
1/2 t cardamom
50 grams powdered sugar
1/2 t lemon juice
2 eggs, slightly beaten

1. Heat the honey in a double boiler and mix in the butter.

2. In a separate bowl, mix the flour, powdered sugar, cinnamon, anise, cardamom and baking soda. Add to the dry ingredients alternately the honey/butter mixture and the egg/lemon mixture. chill this dough for 5 hours.

3. After this, roll the dough to 3/4 inch thickness, cut it in heart-shaped or other forms with cookie cutters. Brush the cakes with egg, place on a greased baking sheet and bake at 350° Fahrenheit till lightly brown.

4. Baked cakes can be decorated with colored icing, sprinkles, minced almonds or other nuts.

Kalitki
(Koliadki or Presnushki)

These are small, open rye flour pies with fillings of cereals, flour, mashed potatoes, cottage cheese, fresh mushrooms, berries or jam.
This most ancient dish is known as Kalitke in the Russian north, as Presnushki in the Novgorod region and as Koliadki in the southern regions.
The name Koliada comes from an ancient pagan festival.

INGREDIENTS

2-1/2 cups rye flour   a pinch of salt
1-1/4 cups water

1. Combine the ingredients to make the dough and roll it out to form a plait. Cut it into round or oval pieces, fill each piece with your choice of filling and place them on a baking sheet.

2. Bake at 360° Fahrenheit for about 1 hour, or until done.

3. After baking, put butter or sour cream on the top of each one. They are eaten with a sour cabbage soup or with sweet fillings with tea and coffee.

Kurniks
(Chicken Pies)

These pies are traditionally cooked on festival days and are served at weddings.
The pastry is molded into all sorts of elegant and decorative shapes
and the filling is piled up in the shape of a dome.

INGREDIENTS

Dough:
12-1/2 oz wheat flour
3-1/2 oz butter
1/2 oz sugar
1 egg
2-1/2 oz milk or light cream
1 oz heavy whipping cream
1/4 oz salt
1/8 oz baking soda

Filling:
1 chicken, finely minced
10 -1/2 ounces mushrooms, finely
   minced
5 eggs, hard boiled
7/8 cups raw rice
1 T finely minced parsley

Sauce:
2 T butter
1 T flour
2-1/2 cups chicken broth
3/4 cup cream
4 egg yolks

Prepare the dough:

1. Work together with your fingers the flour, butter, sugar, salt and baking soda until you have achieved the consistency of coarse cornmeal.

2. Make a well of these ingredients and break the egg into the center, working it into the flour mixture from the inside.

3. Gradually add the milk and whipping cream, form in a ball and let rest for several hours. (the filling and sauce can be prepared during this time)

4. After resting, roll out the dough, line a pie tin making sure the dough is slightly larger as it shrinks while baking. Reserve enough dough for the top. Prick the dough with a fork and bake at 425° Fahrenheit for 15 minutes.

Prepare the filling and sauce:

1. Combine chicken, mushrooms, eggs, rice and parsley.

2. Combine sauce ingredients and mix well.

3. Combine filling and sauce and mound in the partially baked pie shell, cover with the reserved dough. Brushing the undersurface with egg white will help make it impervious to steam. If desired, decorate the top with additional dough cut into shapes. Bake the pie on a cookie sheet approximately 1 hour at 350° Fahrenheit.

The Royal Easter Paskha

Serves 10

INGREDIENTS

1 lb butter
6 egg yolks
1 lb, 2 oz sugar
10-1/2 oz cottage cheese,
3-1/2 oz raisins
3-1/2 oz almonds

3-1/2 oz candied orange and
   lemon peels, grated
3-1/2 oz ground cardamom seed
3-1/2 oz vanilla
1 cup heavy cream

1. Cream the butter with sugar until fluffy, gradually add egg yolks, one at a time.

2. Add the sugar to the above mixture until the sugar completely dissolves. Add the vanilla and cardamom.

3. Put the cottage cheese through a fine sieve twice, then add it to the butter mixture with the raisins, almonds and minced peels.

4. Thoroughly mix the whipped cream into the Paskha and pour into a mold which should be covered with cheesecloth and a heavy dish and refrigerated for 12 hours.

Pelmeni or Pasta Pouches with Filling

INGREDIENTS

Dough:
3 oz wheat flour
2-1/2 cups water
salt, pinch

Filling:
10-1/2 oz beef
10-1/2 oz pork
10-1/2 oz lamb
10-1/2 oz chicken or turkey
2 onions
2 cloves garlic
black pepper, pinch
salt, pinch
2 bay leaves
nutmeg, pinch
1/2 cup milk or cream

1. Mix the dough ingredients together in a bowl and let stand for 20 minutes while preparing the filling.

2. Grind the meats, combine, and then add remaining ingredients and grind again until the mixture is succulent.

3. Roll the dough on a floured surface into a thin plait. Cut into small round pieces using a glass or a jar, and fill each piece with the chopped meat mixture, pinching the sides of each piece together.

4. Fill a large pot with broth or water with bullion cubes, adding an onion, pepper and bay leaves, and bring it to a boil. With tongs, add the pasta pouches, a few at a time, boil each batch for several minutes until they are done and keep them in a covered dish until ready for serving.

Russian Borscht

Tatiana Pavlovna Amineva, Moscow State University, Department of Cosmic Ray
Physics, tasted by her husband, Sergei Slavatinsky,
also of Moscow State University.

INGREDIENTS

meat with bone	butter or vegetable oil
potatoes	fresh tomato or tomato paste
cabbage	salt
carrot	sugar
red beet	spices
onion	

1. Take meat with bone and boil till the meat is tender.

2. Add to the broth the potatoes, cabbage, carrots, beets, onion, butter and spices to taste. Simmer until the vegetables are tender.

Note: If you want to prepare lenten borsch, use the same vegetables, without meat, and add a little more butter or oil.

Ukha iz Petukha (Soup of the Cock or Male Chicken)

During the reign of Ivan the Terrible, so the poet Alexei Tolstoi wrote, three kinds of soups were served to the sovereign: white chicken soup, black chicken soup and saffron or yellow chicken soup.

INGREDIENTS

1 or 2 cocks	carrot
parsley	onion

1. Boil a cock or two with some parsley, a carrot and an onion, and after about an hour, add salt and black peppercorns.

2. Take out the bird, bone it and filter the broth. Keep half the bird in the broth and use the other half for small rasstegais, blini or pies and serve them with the soup.

Zucchini (Vegetable Marrow)

Tatiana Pavlovna Amineva, Moscow State University
Department of Cosmic Ray Physics, and tasted by her husband,
Sergei Slavantinsky, also of Moscow State University

INGREDIENTS

zucchini (vegetable marrow)
bread crumbs
Indian spice (curcuma)
vegetable oil
salt

garlic
fennel
eggs (optional)
cheese (optional)

1. Cut the zucchini in I cm circles, roll in the bread crumbs and fry in the oil.

2. Put on a plate, sprinkle with salt, garlic and fennel.

3. Or, when the zucchini is cooked, add eggs and cheese to the pan and toss together until cooked. Then sprinkle with the seasonings.

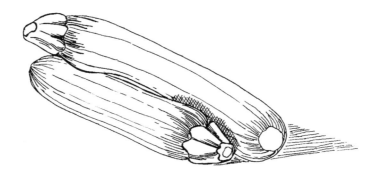

Chaos and Symmetry
present recipes from
THE MEDITERRANEAN AND NORTH AFRICA:

Greece, Italy, Morocco, Portugal, Sicily and Spain

S.S. BURRUS

Agriogourouno Salmi
(Wild Boar in Tomato Sauce)

A trip to Greece by Chaos resulted in this interesting recipe. If wild boar is not available, this works well with any other kind of game.

Serves 8

INGREDIENTS

2 kg (4.4 lb) wild boar meat
1/2 cup butter
6 ripe tomatoes
1/2 cup brandy
whole peppercorn
A little flour or corn starch
salt and freshly ground pepper

Marinade
3 cups red wine
2 carrots, sliced
2 onions, sliced
1 laurel leaf
rosemary
thyme
whole peppercorns

1. Wash the meat, cut it into serving pieces and place it in an earthenware container.

2. Pour the marinade over it and let stand for 2 days, turning the meat from time to time.

3. Heat the butter and sauté the meat. Add a little of the liquid from the marinade, together with the vegetables, add tomatoes, peeled and put through food mill, add salt and pepper and cook slowly for 1-1/2 to 2 hours.

4. Remove the meat from the pot and strain the sauce. Put it in a small pot and add the brandy.

5. Mix a little flour in 1/2 cup water and add it to the sauce. Let the sauce boil for a few minutes and pour over the meat.

Avgolemono (A Greek Soup)

CHAOS was visiting the Democritus Institute in Athens, Greece
and came away with this delicious soup.

Serves 6

INGREDIENTS

8 cups broth (chicken, beef or lamb)
2 laurel leaves
1/2 t thyme
1/2 t marjoram
3 garlic cloves, crushed
2 small carrots, diced

2 celery stalks, diced
1/2 lemon, zest only, grated or diced
2 beaten eggs
1 large lemon, juice only
1/2 cup cooked rice
1/2 cup broad leaf parsley, finely chopped

1. Throw everything into a soup pot, bring to a boil then simmer for about 20 minutes. Strain.

2. Return to the pot and bring to a boil again and add the rice and simmer for a few minutes.

3. Mix together 2 beaten eggs and the juice of a large lemon and add some hot broth to this.

4. Next add the whole thing to the soup pot, stirring constantly. Garnish with the parsley before serving.

Arrosto Di Salmone Al Forno

Inspired by "La Cucina Italiana" December, 1995, Giorgio Gratta, Stanford University

Serves 4

INGREDIENTS

500 gm potatoes
350 gm carrots
600 gm salmon filet boneless
  and skinless
1 leek finely sliced

salt and pepper to taste
herbs, bouquet garni
olive oil
white wine
chopped parsley

1. Boil in salted water the potatoes and carrots cut in wedges slightly crunchy.

2. Slice the salmon filet in half. Put the two slices head to tail and cover them with the leek. Sprinkle with salt, pepper and herbs. Roll the filet and tie with string.

3. Put the fish roll in a pyrex baking dish with the potatoes and carrots. Add olive oil and bake for about 30 minutes in hot (250° Celsius) oven.

4. Add the wine while cooking. When ready, remove string, cut the roll in slices and serve hot, sprinkled with parsley.

Brasato Al Barolo

Contributed by Adriana Giovannini and tasted by Alberto Giovannini,
University of Torino, Italy.

Serves 4

INGREDIENTS

800 gms beef tenderloin
parsley
sage
rosemary
laurel leaf
garlic
onion
celery
white flour

carrot
1 liter red wine (Barolo or Barbera)
olive oil
butter
cinnamon
cloves
juniper berries
salt and pepper

1. Chop together parsley, sage, rosemary, garlic, laurel leaf, onion, carrot and celery. Butter and oil a casserole dish.

2. Dust the meat with a bit of flour and brown it together with the proceeding mixture. Add the remaining spices and wine. Cover and let simmer for about 30 minutes. (You may also put this casserole in the oven if it is covered).

3. Cool to room temperature and slice the meat. Place the slices on a platter and cover them with the liquid, which has been reduced and passed through a sieve. If the sauce is not thick enough, beat in an egg yolk and let it heat, beating constantly.

4. Cover the meat with the sauce. This can be done 2 hours before serving. Heat the platter slightly before serving.

Note: If you cannot find a good Barolo, a bottle of Barbera can be used, which is considerably cheaper. If you take this option, add one small glass of rum to every liter of wine that you plan to use.

Calamari and Linguini

CHAOS found this Mediterranean favorite at a meeting in Vietri, Italy

Serves 6

INGREDIENTS

1 lb cleaned squid
2 T virgin olive oil
4 cloves garlic, chopped
1/4 cup parsley, chopped
1/2 t Mediterranean oregano

1/4 cup dry red wine
28 oz canned tomatoes, chopped
1 large onion, sliced
2 T capers
salt and freshly ground pepper, to taste

1. Sauté chopped garlic and onion in olive oil, add tomatoes, parsley and capers and simmer for about 10 minutes.

2. Sauté squid in a bit of olive oil for 10 minutes and then discard all the juices. Add wine to the squid and simmer for 5 minutes.

3. Combine the squid mixture with the tomato sauce and cook together for about 10 more minutes, until the squid is tender.

4. Prepare Linguini according to package directions for "al dente." Toss sauce with pasta and sprinkle with parsley.

Stuffed Calamari

CHAOS obtained this recipe during a visit to the Amalfi Coast, Italy

Serves 6

INGREDIENTS

2 lb whole squid for stuffing
3/4 cup ricotta cheese
3/4 cup shredded mozzarella cheese
1 T chopped parsley
2 t Mediterranean oregano, divided
2 t Mediterranean basil, divided
2 T parmesan cheese,
  imported Parmigiano Reggiano
1/4 cup chopped almonds

1/2 cup coarse fresh bread crumbs
2 cups mushrooms, chopped and divided

__Sauce__
2 T olive oil
4 large cloves of garlic, minced
1 cup onions, chopped
1 large can tomatoes (28 oz)
1/2 t sugar
Salt and freshly ground pepper to taste

1. Stuff squid with a mixture of ricotta, mozzarella, parsley, oregano, basil, parmesan, almonds, fresh bread crumbs and 1 cup of the mushrooms.

2. Arrange in a single layer in a serving dish that can go into the oven.

3. Sauté the onions and garlic and add the rest of the ingredients to make the sauce.

4. Simmer sauce until thick, about 30 minutes.

5. Pour sauce over the squid and bake at 350° Fahrenheit for 30-40 minutes.

Cannelloni in the Style of Bologna

Signora Boccanegra's Cannelloni

This version came from a wonderful cook. The mother-in-law of Professor G. Puppi at the University of Bologna shared this with Chaos.

Serves 8
INGREDIENTS

Filling:

2 lbs meat, cooked and finely chopped. (this can be beef, veal, turkey or chicken or any left over meat)
olive oil
1/2 cup onion, finely chopped
1 T garlic, chopped

2 lbs spinach, cooked and finely chopped (dry)
1/4 lb parmesan cheese (aged cheese is best)
4 T cream
4 eggs
1 t oregano
salt and freshly ground pepper
grated nutmeg to taste

1. Cook onions and garlic and add spinach. When all moisture has boiled away and spinach sticks, transfer to a mixing bowl.

2. Brown meat unless using leftovers. Add to onion and spinach mixture and add the eggs, cream, cheese, oregano, salt and pepper.

Besciamella Sauce:

12 T unsalted utter
12 T flour
2 cups milk
2 cups cream
salt and pepper to taste

Melt butter, remove from heat and slowly add flour stirring until well blended. Slowly stir in milk and cream and heat, stirring constantly till thick and bubbly. Season to taste.

Tomato Sauce:

Use a prepared sauce and season to taste or mix the following ingredients for a homemade version:
    plum tomatoes
    garlic, minced
    chopped parsley, quite a bit
    chopped basil
    pinch of sugar
    olive oil
Mix ingredients and simmer to develop flavors.

Assembling and Baking at 375° Fahrenheit:

1. Pour a thin film of tomato sauce into a baking dish.

2. Lay cannelloni side by side in one layer.

3. Pour Besciamella over the rolls.

4. Spoon tomato sauce over the besciamella.

5. Scatter the parmesan cheese over sauces.

6. Bake for 30 minutes or until it gets bubbly brown.

Pasta:

Use dried pasta, cook it a little less than "al dente" since it will be baked later. Better yet, use large squares of fresh pasta and roll them around the filling.

Cannelloni Alla Passetto

A meeting in Frascatti, Italy took everyone to "Tre Scalini" on the Piazza Navona in Rome. Here is a favorite from this lovely place, where Bernini's fountain can be admired from every outdoor table.

Serves 4
INGREDIENTS

8 Cannelloni (boiled in salted water, drained and rinsed in cold water, or 8 large squares of fresh pasta)

Sauce #1:
4 T butter
4 T flour
1/2 t salt
1/4 t white pepper
1/4 t nutmeg, ground
2 cups hot milk

Sauce #2
1/2 cup cream
4 T tomato sauce

Filling:
2 T olive oil
3 T minced onion
3 T minced celery
2 T minced carrot
1 T minced parsley
2 cup finely chopped or ground cooked turkey, chicken or veal
1 T salt
1/4 t oregano
1/4 t basil
1/2 t white pepper
3/4 cup dry white wine

1. Preheat oven to 450° Fahrenheit. Prepare the filling: Sauté the vegetables listed for about 10 minutes and add the meat, herbs, salt, pepper and wine. Simmer until the wine is reduced by one-half. Stir in one-half of Sauce #1.

2. For Sauce #1: Melt butter, stir flour, salt, pepper and nutmeg, add the hot milk and cook over low heat for 5 minutes. Fill each of the cannelloni with 2 tablespoons of the meat mixture. Arrange the cannelloni in a buttered dish.

3. To remaining Sauce #2, add tomato and cream. Pour this sauce over the cannelloni and sprinkle with freshly grated imported Parmesan cheese. Bake in the very hot oven for about 10 minutes, or until the top is brown.

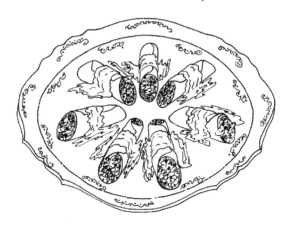

161

Cataplana

Seafood Stew of the Portuguese Algarve,
CHAOS was introduced to this dish at the University of the Algarve, Portugal.

Serves 8

INGREDIENTS

1-1/2 lb calamari, cleaned and cut into rings
1-1/2 lb sea scallops
1 lb large shrimp
24 little neck clams, washed and scrubbed
3/4 cup virgin olive oil
1-3/4 cup dry white wine
1/4 cup finely chopped parsley
1-1/2 lb fresh ripe or canned tomatoes,
  peeled, seeded, and chopped
1 8 oz can of tomato sauce

Vegetable mixture

2 green peppers, chopped
1 red pepper, chopped
1 cup onions, chopped
6 cloves garlic, chopped
1/2 t red pepper flakes or less
1/2 t thyme
1 t basil
6 T fresh cilantro, chopped
Salt and freshly ground pepper, to taste
2 loaves of crusty French bread

Toss all of the above ingredients (except French bread) together until they are well combined.

1. Place the clams in a heavy pot (copper is nice) and pour one-half of the oil and scatter one-half of the above vegetable mixture over the clams and add the scallops and calamari. Spread the rest of the vegetable mixture on top and pour in the wine.

2. Bring to a boil over high heat and reduce the heat to low. Cover tightly and simmer undisturbed for 15 minutes. Uncover, add the shrimp and simmer another 6 to 8 minutes. At this point the clams should be open and the shrimp should have turned pink, but not overcooked.

3. While the Cataplana* is simmering, toast some thick slices of the crusty French bread and paint them with olive oil.

4. Serve in deep soup plates, sprinkle with parsley and pass a basket of the toasted bread.

Cataplana Pork with Mussels

CHAOS in the Algarve region of Portugal.

Serves 4

INGREDIENTS

500 gms pork tenderloin
2-3 T olive oil
25 grams flour
3 onions, grated
1 clove garlic, crushed
400 gms chopped canned tomatoes

1 t paprika
2 t fresh thyme, chopped
200 ml dry white wine
500 gms mussels, scrubbed
  and scraped
2 sprigs parsley
Salt and pepper to taste

1. In a large frying pan, toss the pork and flour together and brown in olive oil for 3 to 4 minutes. Add onions and garlic and cook another 3 to 4 minutes.

2. Stir in the tomatoes, salt, pepper, paprika and thyme, add 1/2 of the wine and transfer to the Cataplana.* Place in a preheated oven at 400° Fahrenheit for 10 minutes. Reduce heat to 325° Fahrenheit for 1 hour.

3. Place the mussels in a large saucepan with the remaining wine and parsley. Cover and shake over high heat for about 4 minutes. Remove the open shellfish and extract the mussels. Add to the pork, stir well to mix and serve immediately with rice or crusty bread.

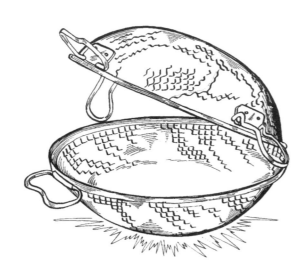

Note: The copper clamshell is the traditional vessel for steaming used in the Portugese Algarve. It is made of hand hammered copper and has copper hinges, handles and clamps. It can be used on the stove or in the oven.

Cataplana Sausage and Bean

Another interesting dish from the Algarve, Portugal

Serves 4

INGREDIENTS

1 T olive oil
175 gms of bacon, cut into chunks
2 onions, grated
375 gms of chorizo sausage, sliced
400 gms can of white or
  butter beans, drained
200 gms of pimentos from a jar,
  cut into strips

400 gms of canned artichokes,
  drained and cut in half
1 T tomato puree
150 ml stock (chicken,
  beef or vegetable)
4 large tomatoes, quartered
2 laurel leaves

1. Brown the bacon in a frying pan in the oil and add the onions. Cook onions for about 3 minutes.

2. Add everything else, mix well and transfer to the Cataplana*.

3. Cook in a preheated oven at 170° Celsius (325° Fahrenheit), for about 20 minutes.

4. Serve with crispy bread and mixed salad.

Note: The copper clamshell is the traditional vessel for steaming used in the Portugese Algarve. It is made of hand hammered copper and has copper hinges, handles and clamps. It can be used on the stove or in the oven.

Chicken with Tuscan Peppers

CHAOS received this simple and satisfying recipe from
Italian friends that live in Tuscany.

Serves 6

INGREDIENTS

1 roasting chicken, about 3-1/2 lb
1 t salt
1/2 t freshly ground pepper
2 t oregano
3/4 t dried red pepper flakes
2 T olive oil

1 green bell pepper, stemmed, seeded,
  and cut into chunks
18-20 pepperoncini, drained, rinsed,
  and left whole
1 lemon, cut in half

1. Heat oven to 450° Fahrenheit. Wash the chicken inside and out and pat dry.
Cut the chicken into 10 serving pieces (2 drumsticks, 2 thighs, 2 wings with some
breast meat attached, and 4 breast pieces).

2. In a small bowl, mix salt, pepper, oregano and red pepper flakes. Sprinkle one-
half the mixture over the skin side of each piece.

3. In a roasting pan, heat the oil and add the chicken pieces, skin side down.
Sprinkle the remaining seasonings over the top of the pieces. Place the pan in the
oven and cook until the pieces begin to brown, about 15 minutes.

4. Remove roasting pan from oven and turn the chicken. Add the pepper chunks
and the pepperoncini. Return to oven and cook until chicken is tender and pepper
chunks are soft, about 20 minutes.

5. Remove pan from oven and squeeze juice from lemon halves over the chicken
pieces. Spoon pan juices over each serving.

Dolce Sformato All'Ananas

(Pineapple Brick)
Contributed by Giorgio Gratta, Stanford University

Serves 4
INGREDIENTS

10 pineapple slices, canned
5 glaced cherries
150 gm unsalted butter
200 gm sugar

1 egg
rum
100 gm lady fingers
200 gm whipped cream

1. Arrange 4 pineapple slices and the 5 cherries on the bottom of a plastic container. Drain and cube the remaining pineapple.

2. Work the butter and sugar until smooth and foamy. Add the egg, rum, cubed pineapple, and crumbled lady fingers.

3. Add the whipped cream to the mix very gently and pour in the container. Keep in the freezer for about 24 hours.

4. Extract the brick from the freezer and keep at room temperature for about 10 minutes before serving.

Fusilli Alla Natale

Contributed by Sergio Natale, presently in Adagir, Morocco.
This can be adjusted for any number of happy eaters.

INGREDIENTS

tuna or shrimp
chopped fresh tomatoes (red)
olives (green)

parsley (if using shrimp)
oregano (if using tuna)

This is a raw sauce and is wonderful over pasta, such as Fusilli.

Although nothing is cooked, the tuna can be canned but must be of good quality in olive oil. If one uses shrimp, they must be immersed in boiling water until they just turn pink.

Italian Bread

Contibuted by Andrea Stryer and Judith Barnard, tasted by Lubert Stryer,
Stanford University and Michael Fain, Aspen, CO

Makes 4 thin baguettes or 2 loaves

INGREDIENTS

4-1/2 cups bread flour
1 T salt

1 T yeast
14-16 oz water

1. Mix flour, salt, and yeast in food processor fitted with dough blade. Add water water through tube while processing until dough forms a mass.

2. Let sit a couple of minutes, then process again until warm (about 2 minutes). Let rise covered for 3-6 hours (the longer the time, the better the flavor).

3. Preheat oven for 425° Fahrenheit (410° in a convection oven). Punch down, shape into 4 thin baguettes or 2 loaves and place into pan. Slash with razor, sprinkle with flour and let rise until doubled, about 25-30 minutes.

4. Place in lower third of oven, throw in about 5 ice cubes. Bake for 10 minutes, throw in another 5 ice cubes. Bake another 15 minutes. Cool on rack.

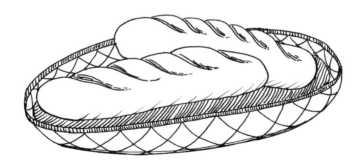

Lasagna Verde al Forno

This wonderful lasagne can be made with white or green noodles, although the authentic version is "verde", which means green.

Serves 6

INGREDIENTS

1 recipe of ragu bolognese
  (see recipe, page 176)
1 recipe of besciamella

3/4 lb lasagna noodles
1/2 cup freshly grated, imported
  parmesan cheese

1. Paint the bottom of a 9x12x3 inch casserole dish with olive oil.

2. Boil the lasagna noodles in a large pot until they reach "al dente" and cool the pasta immediately. Lift out the strips and cool them on paper towels.

3. To assemble the dish: Spread a layer of the ragu in the bottom of the dish, lay one layer of lasagna noodles over this, then spread about 1/2 cup of besciamella on top. Repeat the layers of ragu, pasta and besciamella several more times. Top with ragu and mask with besciamella. Sprinkle this with about 1/2 cup freshly grated parmesan cheese and bake at 350° Fahrenheit for about 30 minutes.

Besciamella

This is necessary for several delicious dishes,
such as Lasagna Verde or Cannelloni in the style of Bologna

Makes 3 cups

INGREDIENTS

6 T butter
6 T flour
2 cups milk

1 cup cream
1/4 t freshly ground nutmeg or more
1 t salt

1. Melt butter and stir in the flour. Remove pan from heat and add the liquids, beat with a wire whisk to avoid lumps.

2. Return to boil and then simmer until sauce becomes a smooth cream and continue to simmer 2 to 3 more minutes to eliminate the floury taste. Season with salt and nutmeg.

Mediterranean Roast Chicken

Symmetry discovered that roasting at a high temperature
produces a wonderful texture and flavor

Serves 6

INGREDIENTS

2 chickens, about 2-1/2 lbs each, rinsed
   well and patted dry
1/2 cup olive oil
2 lemons, juice and zest
7 cloves garlic, 3 chopped and 4 whole

8 fresh rosemary sprigs
salt and freshly ground pepper to taste
1-1/2 lb small red new potatoes,
   scrubbed and halved
1 cup imported green olives

1. Combine the olive oil, lemon juice and zest, garlic, salt and pepper in a large bowl. Coat the chickens well with this marinade and refrigerate covered overnight.

2. Roast at 450-500° Fahrenheit for 1- 1/2 hours.

MIDYE

This is a specialty of Constantinople from the CHAOS Turkish collection.

Serves 6

INGREDIENTS

1 kg large midye (mussels)
1 cup olive oil
2 medium onions
1 cup rice

2 T pine nuts
2 T raisins
salt and pepper to taste

1. Discard any mussels with open or broken shells. Wash and clean (cut their "beards") and drain them. Put mussels in a pot with a little water and steam until the shells open.

2. Heat 1/2 cup oil in a frying pan and sauté the onions lightly. Add the rice and sauté together for 1-2 minutes. Pour in a cup of the liquid in which the mussels were steamed (adding water if the liquid is less than 1 cup) and add the salt, pepper, pine nuts and raisins. Boil the mixture for 5 minutes.

3. Fill the mussels with the stuffing and put them in a pot with the rest of the oil and 1-1/2 cups hot water. Cook over low heat until the rice is tender.

Variation: *Add finely chopped parsley and mint to the filling.*

Moroccan Chicken with Lemons

Chaos has visited North Africa, but this delicious
dish came from a French friend

Serves 6

INGREDIENTS

6 chicken breast halves
1/3 cup olive oil
2 large onions, sliced
1 clove garlic, minced
1 t salt
2 t cumin

1 t paprika
1/8 t saffron
3 lemons, cut in wedges
1 cup green olives
freshly ground pepper

1. Heat oil. Add all ingredients except olives, placing lemons on top of chicken. Cover and simmer over low heat for 1-1/2 hours (chicken will be falling off the bone), adding a little water if it begins to dry out.

2. Rearrange the chicken pieces occasionally so that all pieces get a chance to cook in the juice. Remove the chicken and lemons to a serving platter. Add olives and cook liquid over high heat, stirring until it thickens. Pour over chicken.

A Moroccan Lamb Tagjine

Contributed by Nancy Fried, tasted by Herb Fried, Brown University

Serves 6

INGREDIENTS

1 boneless leg of lamb, cut into 1.5 or 2
inch cubes
2 T olive oil
1 chopped onion
1 clove garlic, minced
salt and pepper
1 t saffron
1 cup water

Sauce:
2 T olive oil
4 chopped onions
raisins
1 T cinnamon
2 T honey
1 T ginger

1. In a large pan heat oil and sauté onion until translucent. Add salt, pepper and saffron. Put lamb cubes in the pan and brown for a few minutes. Add water, cover and cook until lamb is almost done.

2. Remove lamb and brown under the broiler. The tagjine is a special pot that looks like a wok with a chimney, and can be bought in any cookware shop, mail order or on the internet.

3. Reduce the sauce, then add oil to a sauce pan with the raisins, onions and cinnamon and simmer for 1/2 hour. Add the honey and ginger.

4. To serve, sprinkle the lamb with blanched toasted almonds and serve lamb with the sauce on the side, accompanied by rice or couscous.

Note: A shallow round earthenware glazed pot with a tall conical lid that traps the steam rising from the stew (or couscous) cooked in the bottom and prevents drying out in the lengthy cooking process.

Moussakas

This was contributed by Emmanouil Karabinis,
Executive Chef, MTS "Olympic Countess"

Serves 6

INGREDIENTS

3 large aubergines
  (large purple type eggplant)
1 kg potatoes
1 large onion, chopped
1 kg ground beef or lamb
1/2 cup white UNRESINATED wine
1/2 cup olive oil
2 medium ripe tomatoes
parsley, chopped
salt and pepper
olive oil for frying

Besciamella Sauce

4 cups milk
4 T flour
8 T butter
1/2-1 cup grated cheese
  (kasseri or kefalotiri) or 2 beaten eggs
salt and pepper
pinch of nutmeg

1. Wrap the eggplant in aluminum foil and bake in a moderate oven until soft.

2. Wash and peel the potatoes, slice them and fry them lightly. Heat the oil and sauté the onion with the ground meat.

3. Add the wine and the tomatoes, which have been peeled and put through a food mill, the parsley, salt and pepper and let the meat sauce simmer for about 15 minutes.

4. Arrange the potatoes on the bottom of a baking dish, salt them and pour the meat sauce over them.

5. Cover with the eggplant sliced and salted. Top with a layer of Besciamella sauce.

6. Bake the Moussakas in a moderate oven for 30-40 minutes.

Note: According to the traditional recipe the eggplant is fried instead of baked. This makes for a heavier dish.

Besciamella Sauce for Moussakas

1. Melt the butter, add the flour, stir and add the milk, a little at a time.

2. Let the sauce thicken, add the salt, pepper and nutmeg and beat in the grated cheese.

3. Instead of the cheese two beaten eggs may be added.

Oktapodi Me Makaronaki Kofto

Octopus with Macaroni

From the CHAOS Greek Collection

Serves 6

INGREDIENTS

1-1/2 kg octopus
1 cup olive oil
1 medium onion, finely chopped
2 cloves garlic, finely chopped
1 wine glass white, unresinated wine

4 ripe tomatoes (or a large can of
*   peeled tomatoes)*
500 gm macaroni (little tubes about
*   1/2 inch long)*

1. Wash the octopus, place it in a pot (no water is necessary) and let it simmer until most of the juices have evaporated. Drain the octopus and cut it into small pieces.

2. Heat the oil and saute the onion, garlic and octopus pieces. Add the wine, tomatoes (which have been put through a food mill), salt and pepper and cook over low heat.

3. Add some more water and when it comes to a boil add the macaroni. Serve when the macaroni are tender.

Paella

Contributed by Nancy Fried, tasted by Herb Fried, Brown University

Serves 10

INGREDIENTS

1/2 lb medium shrimp, shelled and
   deveined
1/2 lb squid, cleaned and sliced
   rounds
1/2 lb scallops, if ocean scallops, cut
   into fourths
12 to 18 clams or mussels or a
   of both, scrubbed
Lobster tails uncooked
1 chicken cut into pieces, skin can be
   removed
1 lb chorizo sausage
1/4 cup olive oil
1 package frozen peas
3 cups medium or long grained rice

1/4 t saffron
6 cups boiling water
2 lemons, cut in wedges

Suffrido:
2 T olive oil
2 oz lean pork, minced
1/2 cup finely chopped onions
1 t garlic, minced
1 medium red or green pepper cut into
   strips
2 jalapeno peppers, minced
2-3 large tomatoes, seeded and
   chopped

1. Prepare shellfish and chicken.

2. Boil sausage 5 minutes, drain and cut into rounds.

3. Dry and season chicken and fry it in 1/4 cup olive oil. Add sausage to pan and quickly brown.

4. To make the soffrido: discard the fat from the pan and add 2 tablespoons olive oil. Heat and add pork to brown. Add onions, garlic, pepper and tomato, stirring constantly. Cook until most of the liquid has evaporated and the mixture is thick enough to leave a trail when a spoon is pulled across the pan.

5. Preheat oven to 400° Fahrenheit. A 14 inch paella pan is traditional, but a 14 inch wok works perfectly well.

6. Combine suffrido, rice, salt, pepper and saffron. Pour in boiling water and stir. Add chicken, sausage and lobster and stir. Heat to boiling.

7. Bake, uncovered for 25-30 minutes, or until rice is done. **NEVER STIR!**

8. Add frozen peas, the remaining seafood, except the mussels or clams, and stir. Put the mussels or clams on top and bake just until the mussels or clams have opened.

9. Serve in the pan with lemon wedges, and wait for the oohs and ahhs!

Paella de Langosta

This comes from a group of Spaniards at CERN

Serves 4

INGREDIENTS

2 lobsters (2 lbs. shrimp)
3 cups clam juice
1 cup water
1 laurel leaf
1 cup dry white wine
1 large pinch of saffron threads
1/2 cup olive oil
6 cloves garlic, minced

1 T chopped fresh parsley
1 red pepper chopped
2 tomatoes, peeled and seeded
1 T paprika
2 cups arborio rice
salt
lemon wedges for garnish

1. To prepare the lobster stock, combine the lobster bodies (shrimp shells), clam juice water and laurel leaf. Bring to boil, two cloves of garlic and the parsley. Pulse together, strain and set aside. This is known as picado. There should be 3-1/2 cups of stock. Stir in the wine and saffron

2. In food processor combine 1/4 cup oil and 2 cloves of garlic and the parsley. Pulse together and set aside (this is known as picado).

3. Preheat oven to 400° Fahrenheit .

4. Place a 14 inch paella pan over high heat. Add 1/4 cup oil and the lobster (shrimp) pieces and sauté for a minute or two. Add red pepper and sauté one more minute, then stir in the paprika and picado. Add tomatoes and remaining 4 cloves of garlic and sauté one more minute then stir in the paprika and picado.

5. Add the rice and stir to coat and then stir in the stock and cook, simmering vigorously for about 15 minutes until most of the fluid has been absorbed. Add salt to taste.

6. Place the paella in the oven and cook for 10-15 minutes until rice is slightly browned on top. Remove pan. Cover and let stand for 5-10 minutes. Garnish with lemon wedges.

Pasticcio Me Makaronia

From the Symmetry Collection

Serves 8

INGREDIENTS

500 gms macaroni for pasticcio
1/2 cup butter
salt and pepper
2 eggs, beaten

1-1/2 cup grated cheese
besciamella sauce
*   (see page 168 for recipe)*
tomato sauce with meat (universal)

1. Bring plenty of salted water to a boil. As soon as it reaches the boiling point, add the macaroni and stir from time to time. When it is done (al dente) drain.

2. Put 1/2 in a baking dish, sprinkle with 1/2 of the grated cheese and cover with the meat sauce.

3. Add the rest of the macaroni, sprinkle with cheese again and pour the melted butter over it. Top the pasticcio with a layer of besciamella sauce, to which the beaten eggs have been added. Sprinkle the rest of the cheese over the top and bake in a moderate oven for about 40 minutes.

Ragu Bolognese

CHAOS learned a great deal about the cooking of Northern Italy
during time spent at the University of Bologna

Makes 2-1/2 cups

INGREDIENTS

3/4 lb smoked ham, chopped coarsely
1 lb ground lean beef or turkey
1 cup onion, chopped
1/4 cup carrots, chopped
1/2 cup celery
4 T virgin olive oil
2 T unsalted butter

1/2 cup dry white wine
2 cups beef broth
2 T tomato paste
1 cup milk or cream
1/2 t freshly grated nutmeg
salt and fresh ground black pepper

1. Combine the onions, carrots, celery and ham and saute in a mixture of oil and butter. (This is called a *battuto* and becomes a *soffritto* when cooked) Cook for about 10 minutes and transfer to a saucepan.

2. In a skillet, brown the meat, pour in the wine and simmer until most of the liquid has cooked away. Add this to the *soffritto* in the saucepan and stir in the tomato paste and the beef broth. Simmer for 30-40 minutes.

3. Before serving, stir in the milk or cream and simmer until heated through, then add more seasoning, especially the nutmeg. This ragu can be served over pasta, or used as part of the ingredients for *Lasagna Verde al Forno* (see recipe, page 168).

Risotto Alla Milanese

CHAOS learned this from Amelia Ratti, as tasted by Sergio Ratti
University of Pavia

Serves 4

INGREDIENTS

50 gm butter
1 finely chopped onion
300 gm "aborio" rice
boiling broth

salt
saffron
grated parmesan cheese

1. Sauté the onion with the butter in a pan.

2. Add the rice and roast at high heat until shining and transparent.

3. Add the boiling broth, a cup at a time, and let it be absorbed before adding more. Continue stirring with a wooden spoon until the rice is cooked. Add salt, saffron, and cheese, mixing well. Let rest 5 minutes before serving.

Risotto Con Scampi

CHAOS obtained this recipe as a variation of the one in
"Guidacucina" Crostacei e Mollusschi

Serves 4

INGREDIENTS

1 lb rock shrimp, peeled, deveined, and
   cut in half
6 T olive oil
1/2 cup chopped onions
1/2 cup chopped shallots
1 1/2 cups Aborio rice

1/2 cup dry white wine
1-1/2 cups plum tomatoes
2 cloves garlic, minced
2 T cognac
2 T choppes parsley as garnish
salt and freshly ground pepper to taste

1. Bring 6 cups of water to a boil and keep at a simmer. Sauté shallots and onions in 3 tablespoons of oil, add the rice and stir until the rice is coated with oil.

2. Add the wine and cook, stirring until it evaporates. Add the tomatoes and cook for a few minutes and then add the hot water 1 cup at a time and stir until it is evaporated before adding each additional cup.

3. When the rice is almost done, sauté the garlic in the remaining oil. Remove and discard the garlic and add the shrimp. Cook for just a few minutes, until they turn pink, and add them to the rice.

4. Add the cognac and cook for a few more minutes. Remove from the heat, place in a serving dish and decorate with the fresh parsley before serving.

Sea Scallops Provençale

From the Symmetry collection of Provence, France

Serves 4

INGREDIENTS

1 lb scallops
2 T chopped parsley
dash of Tabasco or pinch of cayenne
  pepper
1 medium onion, sliced
28 oz canned tomatoes, crushed
4 cloves garlic, chopped

2 T chopped green olives
1/2 cup dry white wine
1/2 t mixed herbs of the Provence
  (rosemary, thyme, marjoram,
  tarragon, and oregano)
salt and freshly ground pepper to taste

1. Sauté garlic and onion. Add all remaining ingredients except wine and scallops. Cook sauce for 15 minutes.

2. Add wine and scallops and simmer just a few minutes until scallops are cooked. Serve in bowls accomanied by crusty french bread.

Spanakotiropita
(Spinach and Cheese Pie)

From the Symmetry Collection

Serves 4

INGREDIENTS

1 kg fresh spinach
250 gm feta cheese
1 large leek, finely chopped
300 gm spring onions, finely chopped
1-1/2 cup olive oil

1/2 bunch dill weed, finely chopped
1/2 bunch parsley, finely chopped
2 eggs
salt and pepper
500 gm phyllo dough

1. Pick, wash and blanch the spinach. Chop it, after squeezing out the excess liquid. Mash the feta cheese with a fork.

2. Heat half the oil and sauté the onions and leek lightly. Remove the pot from heat, add the dill weed, parsley, feta cheese, beaten eggs, spinach, salt and pepper and stir to mix.

3. Brush a baking pan with oil and line it with half the sheets of phyllo dough, brushing each one with oil as it is added. Put in the filling and cover the pie with the rest of the dough, oiling it as before.

4. Bake in a moderate oven for 1 hour.

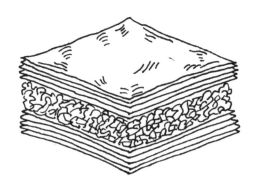

Suppli al Telefono

A cooking lesson by Signora Boccanegra

Serves 4

INGREDIENTS

2 cups freshly made arborio rice or left
  over cooked rice
2 eggs
1/2 cup freshly grated imported
  parmesan cheese

6 oz fresh mozzarella cheese, cut into
  1-1/2 inch cubes
3/4 cup dry bread crumbs
good olive oil for frying

1. Beat the eggs with a whisk and add them to the rice. Fold in the grated cheese.

2. Take a cube of mozzarella cheese and form a ball of rice around the cube. Roll the balls in bread crumbs and place on waxed paper. When all the balls are formed, chill them for 20-30 minutes.

3. Fry the balls in olive oil until the outsides are golden brown. Transfer to a fireproof dish and keep them hot. Serve as a first course and pass a good tomato sauce as topping.

Note: The name is derived from the fact that breaking away a bite of rice will result in a string of cheese, like a telephone wire.

Tiramisu

There are so many recipes for this popular Italian dessert,
Symmetry just wanted to include a simple one.

Serves 8

INGREDIENTS

8 oz mascarpone cheese
1/4 cup powdered sugar
1/2 cup ricotta
1/2 cup heavy cream, whipped

3/4 cup espresso
1/4 cup coffee liqueur
1 loaf pound cake
2 t unsweetened cocoa

1. In a large bowl, beat mascarpone cheese and sugar, fold in ricotta and whipped cream.

2. In a small bowl, mix coffee and liqueur.

3. Slice pound cake into 6 layers. Arrange the cake in a container and sprinkle with the liquid. Spread the cheese mixture over this, top with the rest of the cake, and repeat the process.

4. Sift cocoa powder over the top and refrigerate overnight.

Here is another one:

INGREDIENTS

4 egg yolks
3 oz sugar
1 t vanilla
3 cups whipping cream
2 lbs mascarpone cheese

4 oz Kahlua
24 Lady Fingers
1 cup espresso
shaved chocolate
cocoa powder

1. Mix egg yolks, sugar and vanilla over a double boiler until the yolks have been tempered. Combine whipping cream, mascarpone cheese, Kahlua and egg yolk mixture and whip until stiff.

2. Soak Lady Fingers in espresso to soften. Layer Lady Fingers and mascarpone mixture in small bowls. Top with shaved chocolate and cocoa powder.

Tortoni

This dessert is from Palermo, Sicily

Serves 8

INGREDIENTS

1/2 cup bread crumbs
1/4 cup chopped almonds
1/2 sugar
1/4 t salt

1/2 cup milk
1/2 pint heavy cream
2 T sugar
1/4 t almond flavoring

1. Combine crumbs, almonds and sugar. Reserve 2 tablespoons of this mixture. Pour milk over the remainder.

2. Whip the heavy cream and add the crumb mixture and tha almond flavoring.

3. Fill paper cups (such as those used for baking cupcakes) and sprinkle them with the reserved mixture. Freeze for 2 hours.

Note: Candied fruit may be added to mixture.

Chaos and Symmetry
present recipes from

THE MIDDLE EAST

Israel and Yemen

SS. BURRUS

Akuw'a

Serves 4

INGREDIENTS

500 gm ox tail
1 tomato, chopped
1 onion, whole

4 cloves garlic, whole
hawayij
salt

Wash the ox-tail and remove the hair. Cut into pieces. Place in a pot and cover with water. Add the onion, garlic, tomato, salt and hawayij. Boil for 5 minutes over high heat, lower to a slow flame and leave to simmer over night. Serve hot.

Chicken Soup, Yemen

From the CHAOS Middle East collection

Serves 4

INGREDIENTS

1 chicken, disjointed
1 marrow (zucchini)
1 tomato
5 cups water

4 cloves garlic, whole
hawayij
salt

Boil water in pot. When boiling add parts of chicken, onion, marrow, tomato, salt and hawyij. Cook until meat is tender. After cooking, remove tomato. Serve hot.

S.S. BURRUS

Chopped Herring

Contributed by Bernice Mink and tasted Dr. Barry Mink, Aspen, Colorado

INGREDIENTS

*1 lb herring-skin herring, clean, gut,
    and filet under running water*
2 hard boiled eggs

1/2 green pepper
7 Jonathan apples, peeled
3 yellow onions

In cuisinart, place herring, chop, add eggs and pulse chop for 2 minutes. Remove herring and eggs and chop the rest of the ingredients. Mix all together and chill for several hours.

Geed
(Penis of Ox or Bull)

A three month summer visit to the Weizman Institute in
Rehovot, Israel yielded this exotic dish

Serves 4

INGREDIENTS

500 gms penis
1 tomato, chopped
1 onion, chopped
3 cloves of garlic, minced
1 t coriander

1 t cumin
1/4 t saffron
*salt and freshly ground pepper,
    to taste*
1 T good olive oil

1. Scald the penis and clean it. Boil in a kettle of water for 10 minutes, remove from the pot and slice. Brown the onion, garlic and coriander in the oil. Add the penis slices and sauté.

2. Mix tomato, pepper, cumin, saffron and salt. Cover the penis with this mixture. Cover the pot and simmer over low heat for 2 hours, adding a little water from time to time to prevent burning. Serve hot and season with Hilbeh (see receipe page 186).

Hawaij Seasoning

INGREDIENTS

2 t freshly ground black pepper
1 T caraway seeds
1 t cardamom seeds

1 t saffron threads.
2 t turmeric

Grind in a mortar, mix well and store in a tightly sealed jar.

Note: Hawaij is used to season meat dishes and soups.

Hilbeh
a Yemenite Seasoning

INGREDIENTS

2 t fenugreek seeds
1/2 t zhug (recipe follows)
Purée of 1 fresh tomato

Grind the seeds or pound them very fine. Leave in hot water for 2 hours. Cool, Drain and add zhug, tomato purée and a little water. If you wish to keep this mixture for a few days, bring to a boil, remove at once and cool.

Locust

CHAOS did taste this unique dish

Serves 4

INGREDIENTS

2 kg locusts

Heat the oven and when hot, turn it off. Put the locusts in the hot oven and leave for 6 hours. Remove from oven and dry in the hot sun for one whole day. Before eating, remove head, legs and wings.

Lungs in Gravy

This is from CHAOS at the Weitzman Institute
in Rehovot, Israel

Serves 4

INGREDIENTS

800 gms bull lungs
1 onion, chopped
2 T tomato, chopped

1/4 glass sweet red wine
2 T olive oil

Cook the lungs in water for 30 minutes. Remove and rinse well. Dice. Brown the onion in olive oil. Add the wine, chopped tomato and diced meat. Continue cooking for 30 minutes. Serve hot over steamed rice.

Zhug Seasoning

INGREDIENTS

1 t freshly ground black pepper
1 t caraway seeds
3-4 pods cadamom

4 red, dried hot peppers
1 head garlic
1 bunch of fresh coriander leaves
salt

Grind and blend all of the above ingredients and store in a tightly sealed jar.

Chaos and Symmetry present recipes from
WESTERN EUROPE:

Austria, Belgium, Denmark, Finland, France, Germany, Norway and Switzerland

S.S. BURRUS

Baltic Herring Fillets

Herring is a favorite in Finland where this recipe was given to Chaos by Dr. Risto Orava, Professor of Physics at the University of Helsinki, and his wife.

INGREDIENTS

1 kg Baltic herring
2 cups of fresh dill, finely chopped
1 bunch of chives, finely chopped
1/2 cup of rye flour

pinch of salt
butter or margarine for frying

1. Clean the fish, discarding head and spine.

2. Sprinkle every other fish with salt and pepper and a layer of chopped dill and chives and press it together with another fish.

3. Turn each pair of fish in the flour and fry until golden brown.

4. If you want to serve with a sauce, add cream to the remaining butter in the frying pan and heat it to just below boiling then it's ready.

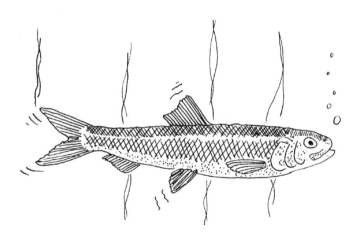

Candied Pear Tart

Contributed by Judy Buchholz and tasted by David Buchholz
of Northwestern University.

INGREDIENTS

3 pears (preferably Comice)
1/2 bottle rose wine
1/2 cup sugar
1 clove
1/4 dried orange peel
3/4 cup ground almonds
1/2 cup sugar
7/8 cup heavy cream

2 egg yolks
1-3/4 cups flour
1 T baking powder
6-1/2 T softened butter
1 egg
1/2 cup powdered sugar
3 large pinches granulated sugar

1. *For the pears*: Peel the pears, cut them in half and remove the cores. In a sauce pan, heat the wine, sugar (1/2 cup), clove and orange peel and add the pear halves and poach until the pears are tender. Allow them to cool in the wine. Makes enough pears for 2 tarts.

2. *For the almond cream:* Combine the almonds, 1/2 cup sugar, heavy cream and egg yolks and mix well. Makes enough cream for 1 tart.

3. *For the sweet short pastry:* Sift together the flour and baking powder onto a work surface and make a well in the center. Place the softened butter, egg and the two types of sugar in the well and mix into the flour, working rapidly with the tips of the fingers. Form into a ball and allow to rest for at least 2 hours. Makes enough pastry for two 9 inch tarts.

4. Roll out the pastry dough and line a 9 inch buttered tart pan. Do not prick the dough. Bake blind for 10-15 minutes at 400° Fahrenheit. Pour the almond cream into the bakes pastry. Slice the pear half into three pieces and arrange them in a concentric circle nine of the pieces. Bake at 350° Fahrenheit for about 45 minutes or until the cream is golden brown.

This is a variation of a pear tart recipe from the Ritz Escoffier Ecole de Gastronomie Francaise.

Caramel Custard

Lillian Ramond, tasted by Pierre Ramond, University of Florida

Serves 6

INGREDIENTS

1-1/2 cup sugar
1 qt milk
6 eggs

1/8 t salt
1 t vanilla extract

1. Preheat oven to 325° Fahrenheit. Place 1 cup sugar in a heavy skillet. Cook over low heat, without stirring, until sugar forms a light-brown syrup, then stir to blend.

2. Use syrup to coat bottom and sides of 1-1/2 quart glass casserole or fluted metal mold.

3. Make custard: In medium saucepan over medium heat, heat the milk just until bubbles form around the edge of saucepan.

4. In a large bowl, with rotary beater, beat eggs slightly. Add remaining 1/2 cup of sugar, salt and vanilla. Gradually pour in hot milk, stirring constantly. Pour into casserole.

5. Set casserole in shallow pan, pour hot water to 1/2 inch level around casserole.

6. Bake 1 hour and 35 minutes, or until knife inserted in center comes out clean. Let custard cool, then refrigerate overnight.

7. To serve, run small spatula around edge of casserole to loosen. Invert on shallow serving dish, shake gently to release. The caramel acts as a sauce.

Chicken or Rabbit
with Mustard Sauce

CHAOS learned how to prepare this with rabbit in Geneva, Switzerland.
It works well with chicken breast, skin removed before preparation.

Serves 4
INGREDIENTS

4 chicken breast halves	*1/2 t thyme*
1/2 cup dijon mustard (Maille)	*1 laurel leaf*
salt and freshly ground black pepper	*1 large shallot*
3 T virgin olive oil	*1 cup mushrooms, cut up*
2 T unsalted butter	*1/2 cup fresh parsley, chopped*
1 T flour	*2 T cognac, for flaming*
1/2 bottle good dry white wine	*1-2 T cream*

1. Pat meat dry and sprinkle generously with salt and pepper. Brush one side with 1/2 the mustard.

2. Heat the oil and one tablespoon of the butter in a large deep skillet and add the rabbit or chicken, mustard side down, in a single layer. Cook until nicely browned. Brush with mustard and turn pieces to brown on the other side and flame with the cognac.

3. Remove meat to a platter and pour off excess fat from the skillet. Add shallot and cook until golden. Sprinkle with flour; stir well and then stir in wine, herbs and Laurel leaf.

4. Nestle meat pieces into shallot mixture and simmer. Meanwhile, melt remaining butter and a little oil, add mushrooms and cook about 3 minutes, set aside.

5. Transfer meat to a heated serving dish. Boil pan juices to reduce slightly and add a little cream. Pour over meat and top with shallot/mushroom mixture, then sprinkle with parsley.

Cranberries with Port Wine and Grand Marnier

Irma F. Sondhelm of Esslingen a/N, Germany.
This is an old family recipe that was always made with Lingonberries.
It has been adjusted for cranberries.

The quantity will fill seven (16 ounce) wide mouth jars

INGREDIENTS

4 12oz bags fresh cranberries
6 cups sugar
1-1/2 cups Port Wine

1-1/2 cups water
1/2 cup Grand Marnier

1. Dissolve sugar in the water. Add a good quality port wine and the washed cranberries.

2. On medium heat, cook until all the skins have popped without stirring. Push whole berries under the liquid with a wooden spoon until all the berries are soft. Use a food mill to process berries until only the skins are left over.

3. Cool a bit then add the Grand Marnier and mix well. Put into sterilized jars and refrigerate, or process in boiling water for longer storage.

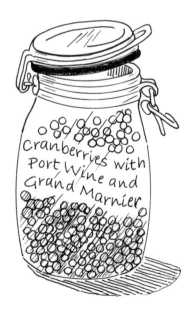

Créme Brûlé with Berries

Nancy Zachariasen, tasted by Fred Zachariasen,
California Institute of Technology

Serves 6-8, depending on the size of the ramekins

INGREDIENTS

4 cups heavy cream
1 oz vanilla extract
8 large egg yolks
6 oz white sugar
2 oz brown sugar

2 large strawberries
1/2 pint blueberries
1/2 pint raspberries
8 fresh mint leaves

1. In a small saucepan, scald the cream. Add the vanilla extract and let steep for 10 minutes.

2. Place 8 ramekins in a roasting pan and set aside. Preheat oven to 300° Fahrenheit with the rack in the center.

3. Beat the egg yolks until blended, add white sugar slowly until blended. Slowly beat the scalded cream into the egg yolk mixture. Strain through a fine sieve and pour the custard into the ramkins.

4. Place roasting pan on the center rack and slowly pour hot tap water into the roasting pan about halfway up the ramekins. Bake until the custards are slightly set, about 20 minutes. Remove and let cool in the refrigerator.

5. When ready to serve, preheat the broiler and set the rack on the top level. Sift an even layer of brown sugar over the custards, place under the broiler until the sugar starts to melt, approximately 1 minute. You can camarelize the sugar with a kitchen blow torch after covering with the brown sugar. Serve with berries and mint leaves.

Dressed Endives

This recipe comes from Eva Derrick, as tasted by Malcom Derrick,
Argonne National Labs

Serves 4

INGREDIENTS

4 medium or 8 small Belgian endives
medium thickly sliced ham or turkey
a little butter

grated cheese
pinch of bread crumbs

1. Clean endives: cut the tiniest slice off at the end and hollow ends. Cut a little more if you do not like the bitter taste. Parboil endives in a little water and drain, saving the cooking and drained liquid.

2. Make a cheese sauce from a little butter, flour and the liquids. Add the cheese until melted.

3. Butter an oven proof dish. Roll each endive in a slice of meat, arrange in the dish and cover with fairly thick sauce. Sprinkle with bread crumbs and bake at 350° Fahrenheit until bubbly, about 25 minutes.

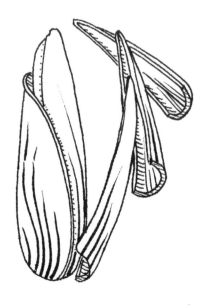

Duck Breast with Red Onion Confit

Carla Berry as tasted by R. Stephen Berry, University of Chicago

Serves 6

INGREDIENTS

*6 medium skinless duck breasts or
   3 extra large "maigrets"
2 T olive oil
1 t ground ginger*

*watercress or parsley
   as a garnish
salt and pepper, to taste*

1. Rub the duck with the seasonings and let stand for one hour. Sauté the breast in a large pan with a little oil, approximately 6 minutes on one side and 4 minutes on the other. The time will depend on the thickness of the duck. The interior should still be pink.
Or:
Grill on barbecue or under a hot broiler, approximately 6 minutes on the first side and 3 minutes on the second side.

2. Cut into 1/4 inch slices on the bias and fan onto a warm platter. Garnish with parsley or watercress. Serve with confit on the side.

Red Onion Confit

Makes one cup

INGREDIENTS

*1 t garlic, minced
1/4 cup shallots, minced
1/2 t thyme
1 T olive oil
2-1/2 cups thinly sliced red onion*

*1/4 cup tawny port wine
1/2 cup dry red wine
1 t sugar
1 T balsamic vinegar
3 T parsley, minced*

1. In a heavy skillet cook garlic and shallot, thyme, salt and pepper.

2. Add onion and cook 5-10 minutes until soft, but not brown.

3. Add port wine and red wine, sugar and vinegar. Simmer uncovered 5-10 minutes until almost all liquid is evaporated. Stir in parsley and cook 1 minute. Adjust seasoning to taste.

4. Chill covered. Reheat before serving.

Filet de Chevreuil Saint-Hubert

This is a traditional French and Swiss recipe. During game season, in the fall, many restaurants in France, Switzerland, Germany, Belgium and Austria feature game. This is a favorite.

Serves 4

INGREDIENTS

1 filet of deer	**Marinade:** *
1/2 glass champagne	1 carrot
150 gms mushrooms	1 onion
800 gms chestnuts	1 bunch parsley
2 shallots	1 t thyme
1 small jar lingonberry jam	1 large laurel leaf
150 ml beef bouillon	1/2 liter red wine
15 gms flour	2 T olive oil
75 gms butter	
4 slices white bread	*you must marinate this filet of deer for
salt and pepper to taste	36 hours

1. Prepare the marinade. If some bones are available, crush them and add to the marinade and refrigerate for 36 hours.

2. The day of the preparation, heat the oven to a high temperature. In the meantime, prepare the sauce. Drain the meat. Peel and chop a shallot and add it to the bones and vegetables of the marinade. Put this in a casserole dish and slide into oven for about 15 minutes to let the vegetables brown. Remove from the oven and add the liquid of the marinade. Reduce this liquid by half over a hot flame, then add the beef bouillon and reduce again by half, always over a hot flame.

3. In the meantime, prepare the chestnuts. Make crossed incisions and plunge them into cold salted water. Simmer for about 30 minutes. Meanwhile, peel and chop the second shallot, clean and chop the mushrooms. Heat 100 grams of butter and add the chopped shallots. After a few minutes, add the mushrooms and sauté them until all the liquid has evaporated. Put this "duxelles" aside and keep it warm.

4. Prepare the "beurre manié." Soften 15 grams of butter and combine with 15 grams of flour. Strain the reduced sauce, add the above "beurre manié" and let it simmer under constant stirring for 15 minutes. Skim the impurities that rise to the surface.

5. Next, peel the chestnuts and place them in a buttered dish that can go in the oven. Moisten the chestnuts with the champagne, cover the dish with waxed paper and slide it into the oven. Leave it there until almost all the liquid has evaporated. Put them in a serving dish and keep warm.

6. Cut the crust off the slices of white bread and cut them into circles. Next, brown them in 15 grams of butter. Put the slices on a serving plate and garnish them with the mushrooms and chestnuts. Keep hot.

7. Cut the meat into 4 portions and flatten them a bit. Heat 25 grams of butter, brown them quickly and place them on the prepared bread rounds. Add salt and pepper to taste and cover them with the sauce that has been mixed with a small quantity of the lingonberry jam. Serve with additional lingonberries or some currant jelly. Fresh peeled peach halves should also be added to the platter.

Flemish Dish of Rabbit with Prunes

Eric D'Hoker, UCLA, who urges that this dish be
Prepared a day in advance.

Serves 4
INGREDIENTS

3/4 lb dried pitted prunes
olive oil for sautéing
1/2 lb bacon, chopped
1 large onion, chopped
4-lb rabbit, cut into about 7 pieces
flour for dredging
pinch each of salt and pepper

3 carrots, sliced
2 celery stalks, chopped
laurel leaf
1 pinch thyme
1 cup good dry white wine
2 T water, if needed

1. Soak prunes for 1 hour with enough water to cover.

2. Heat olive oil in Dutch oven, add bacon and onion on medium heat for 5 minutes

3. Dredge pieces of rabbit in flour seasoned with salt and pepper, shaking off excess flour, and add to Dutch oven.

4. Sauté the rabbit pieces for about 15 minutes and then remove the pan from the fire, keeping it warm.

5. Add carrots, celery, laurel leaf, thyme and the wine to the Dutch oven and bring to a boil. Simmer for 45 minutes stirring regularly to ensure equal heating of all pieces.

6. Add the prunes and their liquid to the Dutch oven with the rabbit pieces and simmer for a few minutes.

7. Cover the Dutch oven tightly, cool and store in the refrigerator overnight.

8. Heat before serving.

Fondue Chinois

As recommended by several experts at CERN, Geneva, Switzerland

Serves 4

INGREDIENTS

3/4 lb lean beef, thinly sliced   *3/4 chicken breasts, thinly sliced*

COOK THE MEAT AT THE TABLE IN A FONDUE POT FILLED WITH A GOOD BROTH. This may be beef bouillon or chicken broth. Have several dipping sauces available at the table and pass these for your guests to spoon on their plates. Also have bowls of chopped onion, chopped shallots, chopped parsley, chopped gherkins and some capers that can be mixed into Sauce Number 1.

Sauce #1: Mix 2 parts mustard with 6 parts ketchup

Sauce #2: Sour cream and horseradish, mix 1 cup to 3 T. Add a little sugar

Sauce #3: Bearnaise.

Sauce #4: Homemade mayonnaise.

Sauce #5: Curry sauce: 1 cup mayonnaise, 1/2 cup sour cream, 2-3 T Garam Massala

Sauce #6: Greek yogurt sauce: add to yogurt, chopped cucumber, scallion, dill, garlic, cumin and a pinch of cayenne pepper.

For Dessert Fondue Grand Marnier

INGREDIENTS

1 cup heavy cream   *6 bars Toblerone*
3 T Grand Marnier

1. Heat cream, add chocolate, add Grand Marnier and whisk until smooth, then transfer to fondue vessel.

2. Serve with strawberries, sliced bananas, peaches, pineapple, apples, pears and cubes of pound cake.

French Bistro Chicken

CHAOS obtained this recipe during a visit to
the École Normale, Paris, France

Serves 4

INGREDIENTS

1 chicken, broiler or fryer, about 3 lbs,
  cut up
2 T olive oil
1 large tomato, peeled, seeded and
  diced
2 large shallots, minced

1/4 cup chicken broth
2 T red wine vinegar
1/4 cup white wine
1 T tomato paste
1 t tarragon
salt and freshly ground pepper to taste

1. Heat oil in a large skillet over medium high heat. Add shallots and cook 3-4 minutes. Add the chicken and season with salt and pepper. Cook, turning until well browned.

2. Remove pan from heat and spoon off most of the oil. Return the pan to heat, and pour in vinegar and stir up bits from bottom.

3. Add broth, wine, tomato paste, tarragon and tomato. Reduce heat to low, cover and cook about 20 minutes.

4. Place meat on a platter and boil down sauce until thickened, about 3-4 minutes. Add the salt and pepper and pour sauce over meat.

Gratin de Chicons au Jambon

Yannik Meurice, University of Iowa

Serves 8

INGREDIENTS

16 small or 8 large
  Belgian endives
16 slices of ham

Besciamella Sauce:
  See sauce recipe Moussaka, page 172
  substitute Gruyere cheese and
  add garlic

1. Cook the endives (in not too much water). Keep the water used to cook them.

2. Start the Besciamella in a conventional way. When it gets thick incorporate the cooking water of the endives, little by little. Incorporate the grated cheese and a tad of garlic, if you like.

3. Roll each of the endives in a slice of ham. Line them up in an oven proof plate.

Halibut with Sauerkraut

Served atop Juniper Berry Butter Sauce
Emil Jung, Chef and owner of Au Crocodile, Strasborg, France
(awarded three coveted stars in the Michelin Guide)

Serves 4

INGREDIENTS

4 Halibut filets (about 5 oz each)
8 oz sauerkraut, cooked
1 cup white wine
1 t white wine vinegar
4 shallots, diced
10 Juniper berries, for sauce

8 T butter
1 carrot
2 leaves of Savoy cabbage
salt and freshly ground pepper
12 Juniper berries, for garnish
aluminum foil

1. Flatten the filets with the side of a wide knife and season on both sides with salt and pepper. Cut carrot into slices and put with cabbage leaves on top of fish filets. Wrap the four portions of fish and sauerkraut in aluminum foil and steam for 12 minutes.

2. In a small pot bring wine, juniper berries, diced shallots, salt, pepper and white wine vinegar to a boil. Reduce liquid to a third. Cut butter into small pieces and stir into liquid, making sure that the sauce does not boil again. Pass through sieve.

3. Remove fish from foil, arrange filets on top of sauce and sauerkraut on plates, and garnish each with 3 juniper berries. Recommended vegetables for this menu: potatoes, snow peas, and carrots.

Helga's Keks Torte

Serves 6-8

INGREDIENTS

4 eggs
200 gms sugar
1/2 t vanilla sugar
1/2 lb palmin (a fat made of coconuts)

4 oz cocoa
1 lb arrowroot cookies (2 pkgs)
  coarsely crushed

1. Melt palmin, let cool.

2. Mix all other ingredients and add melted fat.

3. Line form (loaf pan is good for this) with waxed paper.

4. Chill, slice and serve.

Note: You may substitute arrowroot cookies for Social Tea Biscuits which are like the German "Keks."

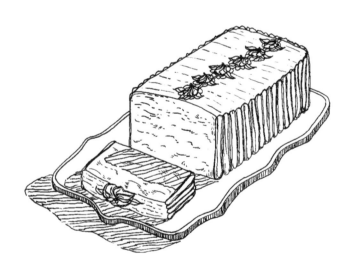

Labskaus-The Fisherman's Meal

This recipe is from Helga Schmitz as tested by Norbert Schmitz,
Max Plank Institute, Munich, Germany

Makes 4 servings

INGREDIENTS

500 gm pickled pork or corned beef
2 bismark herring
2 gherkins
500 gm potatoes
2 pickled beets

2 onions
5 T cooking fat
4 eggs
1 Matjes herring
salt and pepper

1. Boil the meat for one hour in the minimum possible quantity of water, then cut into small cubes or chunks.

2. Cut up the herring, gherkins, beet and potatoes and fry the mixture in hot fat. Add finely chopped onions, pour on the stock from the meat and steam for 1/2 hour.

3. Serve arranged on lettuce leaves, topped with fried eggs and garnished with strips of Matjsherring.

This dish is local to Hamburg and Bremen. A traditional seafarer's meal, it is eaten at the launching of ships. The name originates from the 18th century English expression "lob's course," meaning "fool's meal." It is, after all, a crazy combination of ingredients, but makes an exciting change from more conventional meals. Matjes herring and Bismark herring are available in jars, usually imported from Scandinavia.

Le Coquelet a La Moutarde
Rock Cornish Game Hens

CHAOS has this from the Hostellerie de la Poste Avallon, France

Serves 2- 4

INGREDIENTS

2 Coquelet (Rock Cornish game hens)
2 T butter
1 T dijon mustard (Maille)
1/2 t salt
1/4 t pepper

Sauce:
1/2 cup besciamella sauce (see page 172)
1/4 t salt
1 cup cream
rind of 1/2 lemon, simmered in water
   for about 10 minutes
2-4 slices white bread, cut in circles

1. Preheat oven to 400° Fahrenheit. Combine mustard, butter, salt, and pepper and spread this paste over breast, legs and wings of hens. Put the hens in a buttered roasting pan and roast for about 60 minutes, basting occasionally with the pan juices. When done, cut hens in half and arrange in a shallow pan and keep hot.

2. Make the besciamella sauce. To the liquid in the roasting pan, add 1 tablespoon mustard and cook stirring all the juices in the pan. Add the béchamel sauce and 1/4 teaspoon salt. Stir in 1 cup cream and bring sauce to a boil. Correct seasoning and add the lemon peel, a bit of salt, 1 teaspoon butter and a few grinds of pepper.

3. Sauté 2 or 4 cutouts of bread (depending whether you are serving 2 or 4 persons) in a little hot butter until golden on both sides. Drain and arrange these croutons on a serving platter. Place the hens in the sauce, turn to coat them, and place them on the croutons. Strain the sauce over all.

Le Jambon Chaud a la Chablisienne

In another recipe from the Hostellerie de la Poste.
Ham, which can be quite ordinary, becomes interesting when
served with the unusual sauce.

Serves 12

INGREDIENTS

12-14 lb ham (ready to eat)
1 1/2 cup Chablis (1/2 bottle)

Sauce:
1/2 cup Chablis
2 shallots, chopped
1 T fresh tarragon, minced
*   or 1 t dry tarragon*
1/2 t salt
1/4 t black pepper
4 cups brown stock
1/4 cup tomato puree
4 T flour
4 T butter
1 cup cream

1. Preheat oven to 350° Fahrenheit. Put the ham in a heavy casserole with a tight fitting lid, add the 1/2 bottle of Chablis and bake for 1 hour.

2. While the ham is baking, prepare the sauce: To 1/2 bottle of wine, in a sauce pan, add the shallots, tarragon, salt and pepper and boil rapidly for 10 minutes to reduce wine by one-half. Add the brown stock and tomato puree, bring to a boil and add the flour mixed with the butter. Cook over low heat for 45 minutes, strain into a clean saucepan and stir in 1 cup of cream and 1 teaspoon of chopped fresh tarragon. Correct with salt and pepper. Serve sauce separately.

Mushroom Croissants

Jessica Bender as tasted by Carl Bender, Washington University, St. Louis

Serves 4

INGREDIENTS

2 T unsalted butter
1-1/4 cup fresh firm mushrooms
  (chanterelles, cepes, shitake, morels,
  etc.) trimmed and sliced, or 1/2 oz
  (1/4) cup dried mushrooms, soaked
  in warm water, drained and sliced)

4 T heavy cream
1 T medium sherry
1 package quick-bake croissants
1 egg, beaten
herbs such as sage, shallots
salt and freshly ground pepper

1. To make the filling, melt the butter in a saucepan. Add the mushrooms and sauté them gently to soften without letting them color.

2. Add the cream and sherry, increase the heat and cook until the moisture evaporates. Season to taste and cool. Herbs, such as sage, can be added to the filling. Chopped shallots can also be sautéed in the butter before adding the mushrooms.

3. Preheat the oven as directed on the croissant package. Lay the croissant dough triangles out on a floured surface. Put a spoonful of the mixture at the wide end of each triangle. Brush the pointed end of each triangle with the beaten egg and roll up the croissants so the filling is covered.

4. Put the croissants on a baking sheet. Brush with a little more of the beaten egg. Bake according to the instructions on the package. Serve immediately.

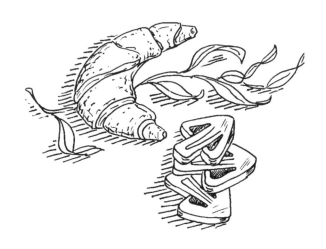

Pâté Madansky

Rena Madansky, tasted by Leon Madansky, John Hopkins University, Baltimore, MD

Serves 8

INGREDIENTS

1-1/4 lb chicken livers
1 lb hot sausage
1/2 chopped onion
1/2 cup sherry
2 eggs, beaten
1-1/2 t salt
1 t spice mixture*

*Spice Mixture:

1/2 t ginger
1/2 t nutmeg
1/2 t cloves
1 t white pepper

Blend the ingredients, a little at a time balancing liquids and solids. Mix again in a bowl. Line sides and bottom of a loaf pan with bacon and pour in mixture. Cover top with bacon and double foil. Bake at 375° Fahrenheit for 1-1/2 hours in another pan with water 1/2 way up the loaf pan. Remove from oven and weigh down with cans or a brick until cool. Serve cold. Keeps about 10 days.

Variation #1: Fill pâté mold 1/2 full and then sprinkle this layer with pistachio nuts about 1/2 cup should be enough. Then cover with the rest of the mixture.

Variation #2: Fill the pâté mold 1/2 full and then sprinkle this layer with 3 oz of drained and rinsed green pepper corns, then cover with the rest of the mixture.

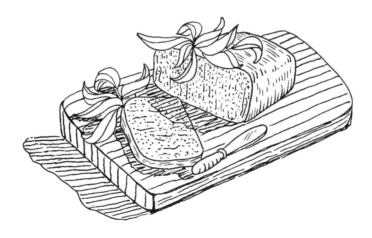

Pears Poached in Red Burgandy

Another fine dessert from France, from the Symmetry Collection

Serves 6

INGREDIENTS

1 bottle good red burgundy
1/2 cup sugar
1 stick cinnamon
6 whole peppercorns
1 small laurel leaf
1 whole clove

2 slices lemon
2 slices orange
6 firm pears (cut a thin slice from bottom
   of pear so it will stand upright)
1 qt vanilla ice cream

1. Choose a heavy enamel or stainless steel saucepan of a size to hold the pears snugly in an upright position. Combine the wine, sugar, cinnamon stick, peppercorns, laurel leaf, clove, lemon and orange slices in this pan. Bring wine to a boil over moderate heat. Simmer 5 minutes.

2. Peel the pears, then stand them up in the wine. Partially cover the pan and simmer until the pears are tender when pierced with a fork, about 20-30 minutes. Spoon wine over pears several times while they cook.

3. Remove pan from heat and allow pears to cool in the liquid. With a slotted spoon, transfer pears to a serving bowl. Strain the poaching liquid into a saucepan. Bring the liquid to a boil and simmer until it has reduced to 3/4 cup of syrup, about 15 minutes. Cool a spoonful of syrup and taste. Add more sugar if desired.

4. Spoon the syrup over the pears. When cool to room temperature, cover and refrigerate. Serve pears alone or with vanilla ice cream.

Pork Loin Stuffed
with Prunes and Apples

This wonderful roast is Danish. CHAOS learned how to prepare it after
a visit to the Bohr Institute in Copenhagen

Serves 4-6

INGREDIENTS

4-5 lb boned, center cut pork loin
1-2 tart apples (Granny Smith) peeled,
  cored and cut into cubes
1 t lemon juice
5 T olive oil
15 pitted prunes

3/4 cup white wine (for soaking the
  prunes)
3/4 cup white wine (for the sauce)
3/4 cup cream
1/2 cup currant jelly

1. In a saucepan, cover prunes with wine, bring to a boil, remove from heat and
soak for 20 minutes, drain and dry on paper towels. Sprinkle the apples with
lemon juice.

2. Make a pocket in the roast, season with salt and freshly ground black pepper and
stuff with the prunes and apples. Tie the roast at 1-2 inch intervals to hold the
stuffing and keep the shape of the roast. For the next 20 minutes, brown the roast
on a medium hot burner on top of the stove.

3. Add the wine and cream and transfer to a casserole, cover with a lid or foil and
slide into a 350° Fahrenheit oven for about 1 1/2 hours.

4. Remove roast to a platter and keep warm. Skim the fat from the liquid of the
casserole, bring the liquid to a boil and reduce to about 1 cup. Add the currant jelly
and simmer for a few minutes. Remove the strings from the roast. Slice the meat
and pass the sauce separately.

Pork Tenderloins
with Danish Blue Cheese Stuffing

CHAOS was at the Bohr Institute in Copenhagen and
learned to make this simple and great dish.

Serves 6

INGREDIENTS

2 pork tenderloins
1/2 lb crumbled blue cheese
8 green olives, chopped
4 garlic cloves, chopped
2 T fresh dill or 1 t dried dill
1/4 cup roasted pine nuts

4 T fresh bread crumbs
salt and freshly ground black pepper,
*   to taste*
2 T virgin olive oil
kite string to tie the meat

1. Mix blue cheese, green onions, pine nuts, dill, and bread crumbs.

2. Cut lengthwise slits in both pork tenderloins and flatten them. Salt and pepper
the meat and place one loin on a flat surface, cover with the stuffing and then cover
with the other tenderloin. Tie the loins together and season the outside of the
roast. Sprinkle with olive oil and place in a fireproof dish. Surround with some
fresh vegetables of your choice and add some small, pre-boiled potatoes.

3. Roast, uncovered, at 350° Fahrenheit for about 1 hour.

Ratatouille

This Provençal classic must be included in every cookbook.
Here is one of the many ways of preparing this popular dish.

Serves 12

INGREDIENTS

1 lb zucchini
1 eggplant
1 lb mushrooms
3 peppers - red, yellow, and green
1 16 oz can tomatoes
3 T olive oil
1 cup chopped red onions
3 cloves garlic, crushed
1 large minced shallot

3 T chopped parsley
3 T tomato paste
1/2 t sugar
2 t salt
1/4 crushed red pepper flakes
1-1/2 t basil
1-1/2 t marjoram
1/2 cup dry white wine

1. Slice unpeeled zucchini. Cut peeled eggplant into 1 inch cubes and cut peppers into strips. Toss vegetables with cut tomatoes and their liquid.

2. Heat oil and add onion, garlic, shallot and parsley. Sauté until the onion is soft. Add vegetables, tomato paste, sugar, salt, pepper, basil, marjoram and wine. Toss and cook covered over medium heat for about 20 minutes. If mixture is too watery, uncover and cook to evaporate most of the liquid. Serve hot or cold.

Red Cabbage, Danish Style

Another recipe from Copenhagen, CHAOS suggests serving this with the pork roast.

Serves 4-6

INGREDIENTS

1 head of red cabbage (2-3 lbs)
4 T butter
1 T sugar
1 t salt

1 cup water
1/3 cup wine vinegar
1/4 cup red currant jelly
1/2 grated tart apple

1. Shred cabbage by hand or in a food processor. Combine butter, sugar, salt, water and vinegar. When this comes to a boil, add the cabbage, toss, bring to a boil again, cover tightly and braise in a 325° Fahrenheit oven for 2 hours. Check occasionally and add water if it seems dry.

2. About 10 minutes before the cabbage is finished, stir in the grated apple and the currant jelly. It tastes even better a day later.

Rosie's Belgium Chocolate Cake

Bea Verbeure as tasted by Frans Verbeure,
Universiteits Instelling, Antwerpen, Belgium

Serves 6

INGREDIENTS

150 gms of chocolate
150 gms of sugar
100 gms of sweet butter
3 T flour
3 large eggs, separated

Icing:
20 gms of coconut slivers
1/2 pint of cream
1 t powdered sugar

1. Melt the chocolate with the butter on a very low flame in a 1 quart saucepan, turn off the flame and add the sugar and egg yolks, while stirring.

2. Beat the egg whites until almost stiff, then add to the pan and mix thoroughly.

3. Rub a cake mold with butter and dust lightly with flour, then pour the mixture into the mold. Bake in an oven heated to 350° Fahrenheit for 40 minutes.

4. After the cake cools, turn the mold upside down on a plate and scatter the coconut slivers over the top. Mix the cream with the powdered sugar and add a teaspoon of melted sweet butter and mix well. Serve the cake with this cream, sugar, butter mixture.

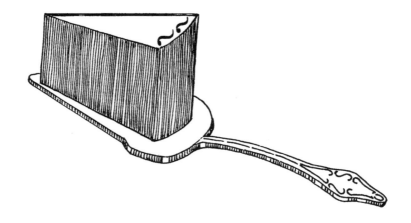

"Rouladen" Stuffed Beef Rolls

This old family recipe comes from Irma Sondhelm, Esslingen a/N Germany

Serves 8

INGREDIENTS

4-5 lbs round steak, sliced very thin and trimmed of all fat; there should be 16 slices of rectangles about 4 inches wide and 8 inches long and no thicker than 1/4 inch

16 T mustard; this should be "Maille" from Dijon, France, or a good brand from Germany, such as "Düsseldorf"

16 slices of thin, lean bacon, with some of the fat discarded, each slice about 8 inches long

16 kosher dill pickles, the "mini" size

4 T flour

4 T olive oil

4 T butter

2-3 cups good beef bouillon

1/2 bottle good red wine

salt and pepper to taste

1. Spread each rectangle of beef with mustard and place a slice of bacon down the center. Place a pickle across the narrow end of each piece and roll the meat around it into a cylinder. Secure each roll with two toothpicks or tie with butcher twine.

2. In a heavy skillet, melt the butter, add the oil and heat to a moderate temperature. Roll each cylinder in flour that has been seasoned with salt and pepper and brown beef rolls on all sides, a few at a time. Transfer the rolls to a heavy casserole.

3. Pour the bouillon into the skillet and loosen all the brown bits, pour this plus the red wine over the beef rolls, cover and simmer on very low heat for about an hour. Turn the rolls once or twice during the cooking period.

4. Next, chill the meat and liquid so all the surface fat can be removed. Return the meat rolls to the casserole the next day, reduce the sauce a bit and then thicken it by adding the usual browned flour and butter (roux). Adjust the seasoning to taste.

5. Return the sauce to the rouladen and heat together before serving. Rouladen are often accompanied by spaetzle or potato dumplings with a chilled cucumber salad on the side. If a vegetable is called for, red cabbage is a good choice.

Sachertorte

This recipe is from the Austrian great grandmother of Susanne Kittel-Habok, Nijmegen, The Netherlands. It is better than the original Sachertorte, not as dry.

INGREDIENTS

140 gms butter
140 gms sugar
140 gms chocolate, melted
3 egg yolks
Stir the above together then add

90 gms flour
Fold into this
3 whipped egg whites

And, if you like, 1 teaspoon baking powder, but this is not necessary. Put this in a buttered 9" spring form and bake for 45 minutes in a moderate oven. When the cake is cool, cut it into two rounds and fill with apricot marmalade. This is also very good filled with black currant or orange marmalade, but apricot is the original recipe.

Chocolate Glaze

1 or 2 bars of bittersweet chocolate

Melt this together with a little water and a teaspoon of unsalted butter and put the warm chocolate on the cool cake and smooth it on as nicely as possible, smoothing it with a knife. If you do not succeed, put loads of whipped cream onto the cake, it is delicious. If the cake is perfect do not forget to serve the whipped cream separately, together with coffee, tea, or port wine. It is a perfect birthday cake, which can be surrounded by candles, held upright in aluminum foil.

*While Susanne was busy writing this translation into English, her dinner burned in the kitchen! We are sorry about the dinner, but delighted with her contribution to the book.

214

Salmon Mousse

Eric D'Hocker, tasted by Jodie Enders, UCLA

Serves 4

INGREDIENTS

1 lb salmon, whole or filets, boned
1 qt or more fish stock or water
3 egg whites
1 cup heavy cream
2 t sea salt
2 t cracked pepper

1 laurel leaf
1 t ground nutmeg
1 large red or white onion,
  finely chopped
4 T butter or olive oil
2 T spices for poaching fish

1. Poach the boned salmon or fish stock and spices for 10 minutes or more, depending on the size of the fish. It should be easily flaked with a fork.

2. Beat egg whites until stiff and mix slowly into the salmon, in a large non-reactive bowl.

3. Stir in the heavy cream, sea salt, pepper, nutmeg and onion. Let the mixture stand for 1 hour.

4. Melt butter or use olive oil to line 4 small molds or 1 large mold and cover with aluminum foil. Fill the molds (or mold) with the mixture and set them (or it) in a pyrex dish filled with 1 inch of hot water.

5. Bake in a 350° Fahrenheit oven until firm, about 30 minutes.

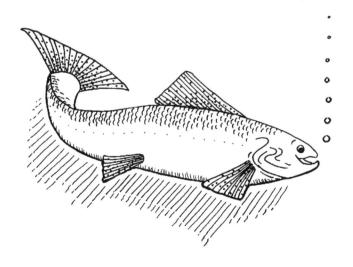

Sauerbraten

Contributed by Irma F. Sondhelm, Esslingen a/N, Germany

Serves 6

INGREDIENTS

*4 lbs boneless beef roast, top or
    bottom round, rump or brisket
1/2 cup dry red wine
1/2 cup red wine vinegar
2 cups cold water
1 medium onion, peeled and sliced
2 carrots, sliced
2 celery ribs, sliced
5 black pepper corns*

*4 cloves
4 whole juniper berries, coarsely
    crushed
2 small laurel leaves
3 T olive oil
2 T flour
1/2 cup water
1/2 cup ginger snap crumbs about 22
    cookies crushed in a blender*

1. Combine the wine, water, sliced vegetables and all spices. Bring this marinade to a boil over high heat, then remove and cool to room temperature.

2. Place meat in a deep crock or stainless steel or ceramic vessel, just large enough to hold it comfortably and pour the marinade over it. The marinade should come at least halfway up the sides of the meat. Add more wine if necessary. Turn the meat in the marinade to moisten on all sides, then cover tightly with plastic wrap and refrigerate for 4 days, turning meat at least twice a day.

3. Remove the meat from the marinade, pat it completely dry with paper towels and coat with the flour. Strain the marinade through a fine sieve over a bowl and reserve the liquid. Discard the spices and vegetables you can retain the onions, carrots, and celery.

4. In a heavy 5 qt. flameproof, non-reactive casserole heat the oil and brown the meat on all sides, turning it frequently and regulating the heat so that it browns deeply and evenly without burning, about 15 minutes. Transfer the meat to a platter and remove all fat. Return meat to heat and cover with the marinade, to which you have added 1/2 cup water. Cook over low heat for about 2 hours. If you prefer, you may cook it in the oven by first bringing the casserole to a boil, covering tightly and placing in a 350° Fahrenheit oven for about 2 hours. Now transfer the meat to a platter and keep warm while you make the sauce.

5. Pour the liquid left in the casserole into a large measuring cup and skim any fat from the surface, you will need 2-1/2 cups. If you have more, boil over high heat until it is reduced to that amount. Combine the liquid and the ginger snaps in a saucepan and cook over moderate heat, stirring frequently, for 10 minutes, simmer until ready to serve.

The Sky and The Earth

Chaos in Germany
This dish can be served as a side dish with all kinds of grilled meats

Serves 4

INGREDIENTS

1-1/2 kg potatoes, diced
1 kg apples. diced
4 slices of bacon

1 onion, sliced into rings
sugar and vinegar
salt and pepper to taste

1. Boil diced potatoes and apples separately in salted water until tender.

2. Drain and add a little salt, sugar and vinegar.

3. Put alternate layers of potatoes and apples into serving dish and keep hot.

4. Dice bacon and fry with onion rings until crisp, and use as garnish.

Strassburger Backeofe

Gail Block and Elias Davis were on a bicycle trip in the Alsace
and sent us this intriguing recipe.

Serves 6

INGREDIENTS

500 gms Mutton shoulder,
  without the bones
500 gms pork shoulder, without
  bones and rind
500 gms macreuse (this is a Scoter,
  a large diving duck which inhabits
  the northern part of the Northern
  Hemisphere)
1 pork tail

1 pork trotter
4 onions
potatoes
garlic
parsley
leek
turnips
salt and pepper
Alsacien white wine

1. Marinate the meat, the spices, finely cut onions, finely cut leeks, turnips cut into large chunks, chopped garlic and parsley and the white wine for 24 hours.

2. The next day, peel the potatoes and cut them into thin slices. In an earthenware casserole with a tight fitting lid, layer the potatoes alternating with the marinated meats and spices, ending with a layer of potatoes. Add all the marinade and some more of the white wine. Seal the lid of the casserole with a little dough made of a mixture of flour and water. Place in a moderate oven for 3 hours. Serve with a green salad.

Thrine's Gravlaks

Tasted by Gordon and Cathrine Baym, University of Illinois

Take two filets of salmon of about equal size and HEAPS of fresh baby dill. The upper part of the salmon is best. Use a deep, flat dish about the size of the salmon filets to place the fish in.

Blend approximately 1/3 cup of sugar and 1/3 cup of salt. Cover the bottom of the dish with dill. Cover all four sides of the salmon filets with the salt and sugar mixture and place one of the filets in the dish, skin side down. Cover with coarse pepper and a thick layer of dill. Place the other filet on top of the first, skin side up. Cover with lots of dill. Cover the fish with aluminum foil. Put something heavy on top of the filets so they are under pressure. Place the dish in the refrigerator.

Turn the filets over every 12 hours for 48 hours. Remove the marinade (the sugar and salt melt and form a sauce, hence the deep dish) and let the salmon sit for another 24 hours. That's it! If you don't have the right dish to place the filets in you may use a plastic bag instead. Just make sure that the marinade does not run out!) Serve on knekkobroed (dark crisp bread) or on dark, unsweetened rye bread with the following mustard sauce:

Thrine's Mustard Sauce

Blend together:

Approximately:
> 1/2 cup mustard (not Dijon, but a good regular mustard)
> 2 T of vinegar (Italian Balsamic)
> 1/4 cup vegetable oil (not olive oil)
> 1/4 cup sugar
> HEAPS of fresh dill finely chopped
>> black pepper

The sauce should not taste too much of vinegar, be about half the thickness of mustard, and be moderately to very sweet, according to taste. The strong taste of dill is *very* important.

As a dinner course, serve the cold laks with hot sauteed spinach and sliced boiled potatoes in bechamel sauce. Serve with wine, or beer and aquavit.

A typical dessert, if served in the summer, is fresh strawberries and ice cream, and in the winter an apple tart with ice cream.

Volaille Pyramide

This recipe was given to CHAOS by Fernand Point of the Restaurant La Pyramide in Vienne, France. The restaurant rated three stars in the Michelin Guide in 1959!

Serves 4

INGREDIENTS

1 large and 1 small truffle, or 2 morel
* mushrooms*
1 large roasting chicken
2 T butter
8 leeks, white part only
8 young carrots
2 cups white wine
6 cups chicken stock
1/2 t salt
1/2 t pepper corns

Sauce:
1/4 cup butter
1/2 cup flour
3 cups broth from the chicken
1 small carrot
1 small onion stuck with 3 cloves
2 T butter
3 egg yolks
a squeeze of lemon juice

1. Loosen the skin of the chicken from neck to the narrow part of the drumstick, carefully separating the skin from the flesh. Insert the thinly sliced truffles or mushrooms, secure skin beneath wing tips and truss.

2. In a large casserole melt butter. Add the leeks and carrots, place the chicken on the vegetables and cook over moderate heat, turning until lightly browned, finish with chicken lying on one side. Add white wine and about 6 cups of chicken stock or enough to half cover the chicken. Add the salt and pepper corns. Bring liquid to a boil, cover tightly and braise the chicken for 1-1/2 hours, turning from side to side at 20 minute intervals and adding more stock if necessary to keep the chicken half covered at all times. When cooked, keep hot in the stock.

3. Sauce: Heat 1/4 cup butter, stir in 1/2 cup flour and cook, stirring for a few minutes without letting the mixture brown. Gradually stir in 3 cups broth from the chicken and cook until the sauce is smooth and thickened. Add the carrot and onion and cook the sauce over low heat for about an hour. Remove carrot, onion with cloves and stir in 1 tablespoon butter bit by bit. Beat egg yolks with a little of the hot sauce and cook, stirring briskly, for about 1 minute. Add a squeeze of lemon juice. Place the chicken in the center of a warm serving platter and surround with the leeks and carrots. Spoon the sauce over the chicken.

White Cabbage with Beef

Helga Schmitz, tasted by Norbert Schmitz,
Max Plank Institute, Munich, Germany

Serves 4

INGREDIENTS

1 kg white cabbage
300 gm carrots
500 gm raw potatoes
300 gm onions

500 gm shoulder of beef
salt and caraway seeds
2 cups beef broth

Put the peeled slices of potatoes, the small pieces of cabbage and the pieces of meat in alternating layers in a pot with a cover. Add salt and caraway and fill it up with 2 cups of bouillon. Bake in an oven at 350° Fahrenheit for 1-1/2 hours.

White Grape Torte

Irma Sondhelm, Esslingen a/N, Germany

INGREDIENTS
Use 9 inch spring form pan

Pastry:
1/4 lb butter
2 eggs

1 T sugar
1 lemon, juice and zest
1-1/2 cup flour

1.   Combine sugar and flour and make a well in the center. Drop the eggs in the well and mix with fingertips.

2.   When combined, mix in the butter, a little at a time, and then add the juice and the finely grated zest of the lemon. Chill the dough for a little while and then pat it into a 9 inch spring form.

Grape Mixture:
4 egg whites
4 T sugar
3/4 lb ground nuts
   (walnuts, pecans or hazelnuts)

1 t vanilla
1-1/2 to 2, white seedless grapes,
   washed and dried

1.   Beat egg whites until foamy, then add sugar and beat until whites are stiff.

2.   Fold in the nuts, vanilla and grapes.

3.   Pour this mixture into the lined spring form and bake at 350° Fahrenheit for 45 minutes to 1 hour.

NOTA BENE

DRINKS AND AMUSEMENTS

Sauce Béarnaise

Back in the last century (the 1970's to be exact) before Chaos' son Steve was appointed Professor at Stanford University in the Departments of Biology and Applied Physics, he read an article in *Nature Magazine* which stirred him to write a letter. Both the article and the letter concern the resurrection of the famous French Sauce Béarnaise. We quote here the article from *Nature Magazine* and the last two paragraphs of Dr. Steven M. Block's letter.

Interparticle forces in multiphase colloid systems: the resurrection of coagulated sauce béarnaise

C.M. Perram*, C. Nicolau† & J.W. Perram‡
Chálet Friedheim, 6386 Wolfenschiessen, Niedwalden, Switzerland
*Permanent address: Julagervaenget 1,5260 Odense, Demark.
†Permanent address: Institut für Strahlenchemie, Max Planck Institut für Kohlenforschung, Mülheim/Ruhr, FRG.
‡ Permanent address: Department of Mathematics, University of Odense, 5260 Odense, Denmark.

The successful preparation of sauce béarnaise is reported. The physico-chemical factors influencing the stability of this colloidal system are considered.

VARIOUS authors have extensively described[1-5] the preparation of sauce béarnaise (SB), the colloquial name for a (hopefully) stable colloidal suspension consisting of a hydrophobic phase suspended in a low pH aqueous phase at different ionic strengths. It is highly probable that the colloidal particles are micelles consisting of a mixture of phospholipids, fats, proteins, cholesterol and various long-chain unsaturated fatty acids. The aqueous phase contains mainly acetic acid and sodium chloride at ionic strengths determined by the initial conditions. Chlorophyll-containing additives, we believe, have little influence on the colloidal properties of the system.

We shall first give a brief description of the underlying physico-chemical principles. Hydrophobic colloidal suspensions exist because of an interplay of double layer repulsion and attractive dispersion forces. The latter are relatively independent of the composition of the dispersive medium and temperature although in some circumstances this assumption cannot be justified[6-9]. The double-layer repulsions arise from the surface charge resulting from ionization of adsorbed acetic acid, in this case, screened by the dispersing electrolyte solution[10]. The contribution to the forces can clearly be influenced by the conditions prevailing in the dispersive medium. The aim of this article is to indicate how an understanding of this interplay of forces can lead to more complete experimental control of the stability of this extremely complex and important system.

Theory

Although we can find no definitive light or neutron scattering data on this system, we assume that the micelles are spherical, and hence that the Van der Waals forces between them are well described by the equation of Hamaker[11]

$$U_A = -\frac{A}{6}\left[\frac{2}{a^2-4}+\frac{2}{a^2}+\ln\frac{a^2-4}{a^2}\right]$$

where U is the interaction energy relative to infinite separation, a is the non-dimensional interparticle separation scaled with respect to the particle radius and A is the so-called Hamaker constant, with a value of about 10^{-12} erg. The number of absorbed acetic acid molecules per unit area of the particles may be predicted from the ambient bulk concentration and a suitable adsorption isotherm[12,13]. The fraction of these which are dissociated will naturally depend on the composition of the dispersive medium, particularly the pH. Furthermore, we can expect that the solvation by acetic acid of the ionic groups on the colloid particles will significantly affect the stability of the particles[14]. If there are N_s, dissociated acid groups per unit area these contribute a surface charge

$$\sigma_N = N_s q$$

where q is the protonic charge. The ionic strength

$$\mu = \frac{1}{2}\sum_{i=1}^{N} \rho_i z_i^2$$

of the dispersing medium will result in a screening of the coulombic repulsion due to the negative charges on the particles' surfaces. The potential of these forces decays with distance r according to an exponental law6:

$$F \sim \psi_0^2[1 - \tan h\kappa L/2]$$

where: ψ_0 = surface potential, k= inverse Debye length, and L = distance between the particle surfaces.

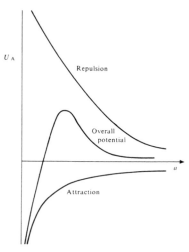

Fig. 1 Potential curves for the interparticle interaction in a multiphase colloid system.

Table 1 Consistency of sauce béarnaise

Observer no. Heterogenous	No. of Samples	Completely homogeneous	Partially homogeneous	
1	2	2	--	--
2	2	2	--	--
3	2	2	--	--
4	3	3	--	--
5	2	2	--	--
6	2	2	--	--
7*	2	2	--	--
8*	3	3	--	--
9*	3	3	--	--

*The authors

The various contributions and overall potential energy curve are shown in Fig. 1. If the height of the maximum in the potential curve is large compared to kT, where k is Boltzmann's constant a T the absolute temperature, then the sauce (SB) will be stable.

This maximum will be increased by the surface charge and reduced by increasing either temperature or ionic strength. This accounts for the empirical observation that the application of multivalent ions has never been recommended in the manufacture of *sauce béarnaise*. Only the increase of s can have a beneficial influence on the stability of the product.

Experimental methods

Commercially available reagents (vinegar, onion, egg yolks, butter, parsley, tarragon, *herbes de Provence*, mustard, pepper, NaCl and alpine water (H_2O) were used, according to ref. 3. We do not expect that our conclusions would have been altered if the alternative procedures[1,2,4,5] had been used. In our hands, heavy coagulation was observed despite vigorous stirring and careful temperature control ($\pm5K$). When coagulation occurs, other authors recommended discontinuation of the experiment[1-5]. However, based on the above theoretical considerations, we decided to add, with extremely vigorous stirring, a further quantity of the commercially available acetic acid solution, and the results confirmed our theoretical predictions.

Results and discussion

After addition of acetic acid, and as vigorous stirring proceeded, the heterogeneous phase soon assumed the expected homogeneous consistency. Examination of the resulting preparation was immediately undertaken by a significant number of trained observers. The results of this examination are listed in Table 1. To our knowledge, this is the first successful attempt to resurrect a sauce béarnaise based on the theory of the stability of lyophobic colloid10.

Thanks are due to Drs K. Hildenbrand, A. Reimann and to M. Hildenbrand, V. Hallmann, H. Dittrich and I. Hengst for agreeing to take part in the experiment.

1. Brillat-Savarin, A. La physiologie du goût 115 (Flammarion, Paris, 1929).
2. Wilmenrod, C. Französische Küche 65 (Vollmer, Wiesbaden-Berlin, 1973).
3. Bertholle, L. Die geheimen Rezepte der besten Restaurants Frankreichs, 489 (Hallwag Bern, Stittgart. 1976).
4. Larousse (ed.) Larousse Gastronomique (Paris 1962).
5. Banzer-Friebel in Die Hotel- und Restaurantionsküche (ed. Friebel, C) 84 (Fachbuchverlag Dr. Planneberg. Giesen, 1974).
6. Barouch, E. Perram, J. W & Smith, E.R. Chem. Phys. Lett 19, 131-133 (1973).
7. Barouch E. Perram, J. W & Smith, E.R. Stud. Appl. Mathematics 11, 175-186 (1973).
8. Barouch E. Perram, J. W & Smith, E.R. Proc. R. Soc. A334, 49-55 (1973).
9. Barouch E. Perram, J. W & Smith, E.R. Proc. R. Soc. A334, 59-71 (1973).
10. Verwey, E.J. W. & Overbeek, J.T.G. Theory of the Stability of Lyophopic Colloids 139 (Elsevier, Amsterdam, 1948).
11. Hamaker, H.C. Physica 4, 1058-1067 (1931).
12. Langmuir, I. J Am. Chem Soc. 38, 2221 (1916).
13. Perram, J.W. & Smith, E.R. Proc. R. Soc. A (in the press).
14. Nicolau, C., Dreskamp , H. & Schulte-Frohlinde, D FEBS Lett. 43, 148-150 (1974).

Following is an excerpt from Dr. Steven M. Block's letter to *Nature Magazine* dated January 17, 1978.

"This may have been "the first successful attempt to resurrect a 'sauce béarnaise' based on the theory of the stability of lyophobic colloid", but it does not represent the first empirical resurrection. Indeed, recovery of *sauce béarnaise* based on the addition of water alone was recommended by James Beard[1] as early as 1959. Beard's technique has been used in my own laboratory with notable success.

Finally, the reversibility of this type of coagulation appears to have been noted as early as 1477, when Thomas Norton worte:[2] "Coagulation is noe forme substaniall, But onlie passion of things material.""

[1]Beard, James & Calvert, Isabel The James Beard Cookbook (Dell Publications, New York 1959). p. 401
[2]Norton, Thomas The Ordinall of Alchimy (1477) as quoted in The Oxford English Dictionary, Compact Den. (Oxford University Press, Oxford 1971). p.477

Dandelion Wine

Contributed by Linda Hodges, University of Iowa.
According to Linda, Colorado dandelions are far superior in this wine recipe
Perhaps it is the spectacular high altitude hike to find the blossoms

INGREDIENTS

1 gal dandelion blossoms
3 oranges
1 lemon
3 lbs of sugar

gingerroot
1/2 cake yeast
1 slice of rye bread,
thinly sliced

1. Pour one gallon of boiling water over the dandelion blossoms and steep for 3 days.

2. Strain through cheese cloth and squeeze out all juice.

3. Boil squeezed juice along with juice and peel of oranges, lemon and gingerroot and 3 pounds of sugar for 20 minutes. Cool.

4. Pour mixture into a crock.

5. Spread yeast on the slice of rye bread and float the bread on top of the wine. Keep the crock in a warm, dark room for 6 days.

6. Put the wine into individual bottles and cork.

7. If you made it in the summer, serve it after Christmas.

Holiday Fruit and Drink Cake

Anonymous committee at an anonymous University.

Makes 1 Fruitcake

INGREDIENTS

1 cup of water
1 cup of sugar
4 large brown eggs
2 cups of dried fruit
1 t salt

1 cup of brown sugar
1 cup butter
Lemon juice
1 cup of nuts
1 bottle of whiskey

1. Sample the whiskey to check for quality

2. Take a large bowl. Check the whiskey again. To be sure it is the highest quality, pour one level cup and drink. Repeat

3. Turn on the electric mixer, beat one cup of butter in a large fluffy bowl. Add one teaspoon of sugar and beat again.

4. Make sure the whiskey is still okay. Cry another tup.

5. Turn off the mixer. Beat two leggs and add to the bowl and chuck in the cup of dried fruit. Mix on the turner. If the fried druit gets stuck in the beaterers, pry it loose with a drewscriver.

6. Sample the whiskey to check for tonsisticity.

7. Next, sift two cups of salt. Or something. Who Cares? Check the whiskey. Now sift the lemon juice and strain your nuts. Add one Table. Spoon. Of sugar or something. Whatever you can find.

8. Grease the oven. Turn the cake tin to 350° Fahrenheit. Don't forget to beat off the turner. Throw the bowl out of the window.

9. Check the whiskey again and go to bed.

La Grolla* Di Amicizia or The Cup of Friendship

Valle d'Aosta, Italia, aka, Café A La Valdotaine

The only problem CHAOS has with this is that it takes a trip to the University of Torino, followed by a few hours of car ride to get to the Valle d'Aosta where the proper vessel is sold and where one can find the high quality grappa necessary for this wonderful beverage! The vessel must be prepared in the traditional Valle d'Aosta fashion. The wood is sealed with boiling red wine, which is then discarded, a sorry waste of good red wine. It is now ready for immediate use!

INGREDIENTS

6 parts espresso coffee
1 part grappa, flavored with
   orange peel

1 part Cognac
A few tablespoons of sugar
1 part Grand Marnier or triple sec or
   Cointreau

1. In a pot, mix all above ingredients and heat. Pour into a "grolla".

2. Pour some sugar all around the moistened opening.

3. Light the liquid and with a spoon, moisten the sugar with the flaming liquid until it caramelizes, then push it into the vessel.

4. Cover the vessel, thus putting out the flame. There is enough alcohol present to sterilize every little opening.

5. Pass this around the table, where everyone sips from the openings.

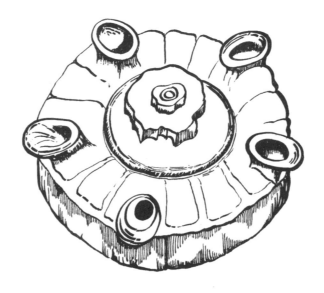

*The grolla.

Quick and Easy Homemade Ice Cream

Kevin R. Forkey, Physics Lab Supervisor at Williams College in Massachusetts was inspired by an article in *Scientific American* Magazine on making ice cream using liquid nitrogen. He has a website featuring this recipe as a favorite demonstration that he provides for about 20 hungry students. He says that it ties in nicely with thermodynamics and phase changes

This recipe is for ~1/2 gallon of strawberry ice cream

INGREDIENTS

Cream Base:
4 cups heavy cream
1-1/2 cups half & half cream
1-3/4 cups of sugar

Berries
1 qt fresh strawberries or other berries
 (mashed)
1/2 cup sugar
Ice cream cones for serving
2-1/2 to 3 liters liquid nitrogen

1. Keep all the ingredients cold!! Make sure the sugar is dissolved in the cream base.

2. Pour the cream base into a large metal bowl. Add one or both liters of the liquid nitrogen and stir vigorously.

3. When the cream has thickened, add the berry mixture and more liquid nitrogen if needed.

4. Continue to stir, using a wooden spoon (a metal spoon will break) until the nitrogen has evaporated and the fog it has created disappears.

5. Serve up the ice cream in the cones and enjoy a real treat.

Note: This recipe does not keep and is best consumed immediately. Melting can be stopped by adding more liquid nitrogen.

Tenor a L'Orange

Anonymous group of singing wives of physicists

INGREDIENTS

At least 2 good-size tenors
20 gals High-C orange juice
olive oil

garlic
6 boxes Portamento noodles

1. If you announce that you are going to serve tenor, you'll attract a big crowd, so be prepared for at least two!

2. It used to be difficult to catch several tenors because they are, by nature, nocturnal animals who avoid others of their species. Lately, however, they have changed their habits and can usually be found in groups of three. They are easiest to capture in the summer when they can be found frequenting outdoor stadiums. Less well known examples can be captured by using vocal students or fans as bait. (Females are usually best, but there are cases where males work better).

3. Once the tenor has been caught, dry off carefully all the sweat from the last aria.

4, Remove the stomach, which is full of ill-digested phrases and swallowed consonants and would make the casserole lid impossible to shut anyway.

5. Pull the recording contract out of his clenched fist. (You may have to cut the hand off). In rare cases, the recording contract may be tattooed on his chest.

6. If the tenor is German, remove the throat which is so tied up in knots as to be indigestible.

7. The major danger in cooking tenor is that the head, which is empty, will collapse. Stuff it with a mixture of parsley and paper money. American dollars work best, but German marks, lira, English pounds and French and Swiss francs are acceptable too.

8. Marinate overnight in olive oil and garlic. (Only necessary in the American or northern European variety; with the Mediterranean ones this step can be skipped).

9. In a big casserole put a layer of portamento, a kind of thin spaghetti with little balls, referred to as nodes on either end. Lay the tenor on top of the portamenti, but be careful: There is a new kind of tenor, often French, which turns sour in contact with portamento.

10. Cover with High-C orange juice, and bake at high heat in the oven. When the High-C boils, it fills up the lung capacity on the tenor, who then lets out a strangled cry which sounds somewhat like "All'armi!"

11. This means the tenor can be served. Bon apetit.

Two Radical Recipes from Rosie

Rosie Colgate, tasted by Sterling Colgate,
Los Alamos, New Mexico

Serves 2

INGREDIENTS

1.   Lace Cream Cheese with lots of minced garlic. Serve with crackers. Then take a shot of rum, pour over ice and add lime and sugar to taste. Add water only as you drink it.

2.   Buy a loaf of sour dough round from the Bakery in Aspen, spread with garbonzola from Smith's in Los Alamos, New Mexico. Place piece of white sliced onion and some lettuce on it and eat after skinny dipping in Hunter Creek beaver pond.

Introductory Thermodynamics for Martini Drinkers (with Laboratory Exercises)

by Peter J. Carrato PhD, P.E., S.E.
Illustrations from the historical archives and by P.J. Carrato and P.Todd

The scientific study of martini making has a long yet poorly documented history. Flemish monk Paulus Gloyens described the effects of seasonal temperature changes on the palatability of alcohol flavored with herbs and berries as early as 1641. His diary, destroyed during the first battle of the Somme in 1915, noted that this gin-like elixir produced a feeling of *gemütlichkeit* (relaxed, friendly exhilaration) when consumed on a cold winter's night. this is the first written account of an ice-cold bone dry relieving the tensions of the working world, even that exasperating feeling that comes from a hard dy of monking.

The First Scientific Martini

A French chemist André Gillespie first applied the scientific method to martini mixing. His classic work *Spiritus Fortis Invius Matutinus et Vespertinus*[1] devotes an entire folio to the intricacies of producing a drink of gin and various wines and brandies. Some mixologists speculate that the term martini was taken from the title of this work, by the uneducated rabble of the era mistaking the Latin word for morning to be the name of the beloved cocktail. As a result of numerous trials he concluded the less sweet to extremely dry wines and brandies provided the best complement to the gin available at that time. As noted in Gillespie's master work, the results of these experiments were designed, and the results interpreted, based on his own personal taste. As with all French science, the methods of measurement are not easily challenged.

A Triumph of German Engineering

It was up to the Germans to apply the science of Thermodynamics to all aspects of bartending. During the years between World War I and World War II, the heyday of the martini, the Reinheitsgebot Institut' auf die Wärmekraftlehre, directed by Doktor Johann Gruber; Dpl. Ing., established the state of the art in shaker technology.[2,3] The good doktor used the First Law of Thermodynamics and an accute understanding of Heat Transfer to develop what he called the *Vorrichtunggruber* or, loosely translated, the Gruber Device. This ultimate cocktail shaker, shown in figure 1, used the best pressure vessel design techniques of the day.

Design of the *Vorrichtunggruber*

The cylindrical body is capped by torospherical shells. The seal between the mating pieces of the shaker employed tight tolerance (measurements were precise to .001 mm) in machining the parts coupled with a sealing detail using double O-rings of the finest India rubber. Fire glazed refractory ceramic, the same material used to line blast furnaces in the Ruhr Valley, was used to create the 10mm thick walls of the vessel. It was sized to accommodate two drinks of 180 ml, a volume of ice four times greater than that of the liquid, and a volume of air twice that of the liquid-ice mixture. A length-to-diameter ratio of 4:1 was established to facilitate manufacturing the shaker.

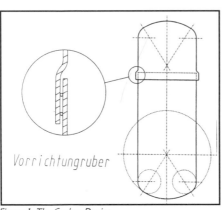

Vorrichtungruber

Figure 1. The Gruber Device

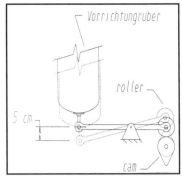

Figure 2. Schematic of Shaking Apparatus

Cocktail Thermodynamics

Before one can truly appreciate the beauty of the Gruber Device an understanding of the First Law of Thermodynamics is required. The First Law can be used to predict the *flow of heat* in a system.[4] It is also useful in predicting group dynamics of a cocktail party. In the case of the martini-shaker system, the goal is to remove as much heat from the gin and vermouth as possible, whereas at a cocktail party one's goal is heat transfer to a selected member of the opposite sex.

First Law[5]—When a closed system is altered adiabatically, the work is the same for all possible paths which connect two given equilibrium states.

A few definitions are in order. The word *system* as used in this law is a three dimensional region of space bounded by any arbitrary surface, in other words what is inside the shaker. An *adiabatic* process is one that only involves work, or a process in which heat is neither added nor removed from the system. *Work*, in this context, involves the moving of a weight through a distance. Moving a cocktail shaker up and down is doing work. Simply holding a glass of gin off the ground is not, in the purest sense, work. An *equilibrium state* is a balance of temperature and pressure, and a *path* is a series of intermediate temperatures and pressures leading up to equilibrium. Equilibrium State 1 is when the gin, vermouth and ice are placed into the shaker. Equilibrium State 2 occurs immediately after shaking the mixture. The path from State 1 to State 2 consists of the intermediate temperatures and pressures inside the vessel during the shaking process.

When constructing the Gruber Device, its inventor strove to produce a truly adiabatic system by creating a pressure tight container that does not transfer heat to its surrounding environment. In fact, the refractory material use for the exterior of the vessel's walls did not measurably change temperature while mixing a standard martini. This is quite different from what happens when using a stainless steel or silver shaker, which can often become too cold to hold when shaking up a favorite cocktail.

Dr. Gruber believed that by keeping his device pressure tight, the humidity in the air would condense into water as the trapped air cooled from exposure to the icy mixture, resulting in a drop in the internal pressure. Based on the Ideal Gas Law (a corollary to the First Law), this would also cause the temperature to proportionally decrease. He expected to achieve a final equilibrium state at temperatures lower than possible for ice, gin and vermouth mixed in an open container.

The Cocktail Experiments

Gruber's experiments did result in martinis as cold as -6.5 C, however the expense of developing and manufacturing the *Vorrichtunggruber*, along with the auxiliary shaking equipment and instrumentation, was phenomenal. High tariffs on British gin and the rise of National Socialist party caused funding to dry up in 1930, and most of Gruber's equipment was appropriated for paramilitary purposes. He spent the war years trying to make a gin substitute from a turnip and cabbage liquor flavored with alpine flowers. Doktor Gruber died a broken man in Tijuana attempting to set up a Mexican franchise for turnip gin.

The Fatal Flaw

The fatal flaw in Doktor Gruber's research was the method he used for shaking his magnificent device. Before being appointed to the Institut' aud die Wärmekraftlehre, Gruber had worked for Daimler Benz A.G., studying the thermodynamic efficiency of internal combustion engines. With this background it was only natural to develop a cam and roller apparatus that would regularly oscillate the ceramic vessel without producing undue impact forces on the relatively brittle container. A schematic of this shaking aparatus is shown in Figure 2.

Note that the maximum amplitude of agitation is only 5 cm (approximately 2 inches). Although the servo-controlled electric motor, coupled with the cam and roller mechanism, epitomized German engineering, it did not replicate true martini shaking. It was up to our team of real world american engineers to take the study of martini thermodynamics out of the sterile laboratory setting and bring it back into the bar room.

Normal Friday Afternoons

The Following experiments were performed under carefully controlled conditions. However, they have been designed to be easily reproduced during a normal Friday afternoon happy hour. The purpose of our testing was to determine the physical parameters that have the most influence on producing the coldest possible martini. We first established a comprehensive list of potentially critical physical parameters. Next an experimental program to systemically study each one's effect was developed, including sample size, instrumentation, data collection, quality assurance and data reduction techniques. With our trusty data sheets in hand, and a fresh bottle of gin and tray full of ice cubes in hand, it was time to go into the lab.

To the Lab We Go

To provide a base line for subsequent experiments, we initiated a series of side by side tests of shaken vs stirred martinis. Under this testing regime we quickly determined that shaking consistently produces martinis that are between 1.65 and 2.03 C colder than those produced by stirring. In-glass temperatures near -4.5 C were commonly measured. Perhaps Gruber's hypothesis based on the classic pressure-volume-temperature relationship was correct. It was purely a chance observation and an overpowering thirst for knowledge that drove us to refine our tasting program in order to challenge his proposition.

A Cap, A Lapse, A Determination

After straining out a batch of particularly dry martinis, one of the lab staff inadvertently replaced the cap on the shaker and left it on the counter, rather than cleaning and drying it in preparation for the next test. Lapses in following establibled procedures are common in the martini lab. After collecting data and settling down to enjoy its handiwork, the research team was shocked as the cap forcibly ejected from the top of the shaker to a height of over 150 mm. It was quickly determined that during the approximately eight minute period the vessel sat on the counter, the temperature of the trapped air had risen to the point where the resulting system pressure could no longer be contained.

How Far is Enough?

Clearly Gruber had been on the right track, but had he taken his experimental work far enough? We now limited our attention to those parameters that describe the work done while shaking. Given the direct relationship between work (weight moved through a distance) and energy, we quickly determined that measuring the number of shaking cycles and the distance traveled on each stroke was the critical data required.

Cold, Clear Results

Results of this expanded series of tests were conclusive. The more you shake a martini the colder it gets! This is clearly shown in Figure 3, which graphs shaking energy versus in-glass temperature. Collecting 7 data points for this graph in a single laboratory session required teamwork, perserverance, and time off from work the next day. Using the instructions given in Appendix A the reader can reproduce the above experiments, or if so inclined study other parameters. However, our conclusion for preparing the perfect martini is as follows:

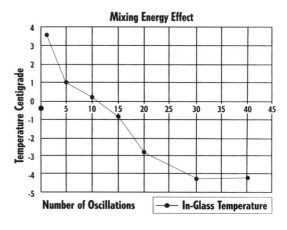

Figure 3. Results of Mixing Energy Tests

The Perfect Martini

INGREDIENTS FOR 2 MARTINIS

6 oz gin   •   ½ oz vermouth
12 to 14 standard ice cubes (approximately 4 cm X 4.5 cm X 3 cm)
Garnish to taste (almond stuffed olives recommended)

PROCESS

1. Place all liquid ingredients in a stainless steel shaker (approximately 1 qt)
2. Shake up and down (approximately 8 inches) 30 times in 12 seconds
3. Strain, garnish, and enjoy

References

1. *Spiritus Fortis Invius Matutinus et Vespertinus*, A. Gillespie, Historie de l'Académie, Paris, 1848.
2. *Allgemeinen Theorie aus Mischun* Reinheitsgebot Institut' auf die Wärmekraftlehre, Bericht 23-02, Heidelberg, 1923.
3. *Experimentieren mit Vorrichtunggruber*, Reinheitsgobot Institut' auf die Wärmekraftlehre,,Bent 25-11 Heidelberg, 1925.
4. *Principles of Heat Transfer*, F. Krieth, International Textbook Co., NY, 1965.
5. *Thermodynamics*, K. Wark, McGraw-Hill Book Co., NY, 1966.

Appendix A—Experimental Procedure

Equipment

1. Timer that measures in seconds for timing the duration of shaking.
2. Meter stick to determine the amplitude of the shaking motion.
3. Imersible thermometer that measures down to -10°C for measuring the martini and freezer temperature.
4. Scale that weighs in grams for determining the weight of the ice, gin, vermouth, shaker system.
5. Hygrometer for determining relative humidity.
6. Barometer for measuring air pressure.
7. Thermometer for measuring air temperature.
8. Measuring cup graduated in milliliters for determining volumes of the shaker, and ice.

Procedure

First select a parameter that is interesting and which can be practically studied. For example if sources for two different shapes of ice cubes are readily available you could explore this fascinating ice variable.

Next assemble a research team comprised of friends, neighbors, your bowling team. A group of at least three is recommended, as you will need a mixer, a data collector, and an instrumentation technician.

Convene a planning session where an experimental program is finalized. If studying ice shape you may decide to do a lab session of stirred martinis, one for each available shape, followed by a second lab repeating the experiments using a shaker.

Let's get into the laboratory! Mix up cocktails, carefully following the planned program of experimentation. Collect the appropriate data using the form at the end of this Appendix.

Finally analyze the results of your testing and use this information to produce better, bolder, colder, martinis.

MARTINI DATA SHEET   date _____ time _____

LAB GROUP MEMBERS:
1) _____
2) _____
3) _____

AMBIENT CONDITIONS:
Temperature _____
Pressure _____
Relative Humidity _____

MARTINI PARAMETERS:

Freezer Temp. _____°C
Number of Standard Ice Cubes _____

Standard Mix, Martinis for 2:
   6 oz London Dry Gin & ½ oz Vermouth

MIXING ENERGY:

SHAKING
Weight of Shaker_____ gm
Amplitude_____ mm
Cycles per second _____
Duration _____ sec

STIRRING
Diameter of Stirrer_____ mm
Submerged Length _____ mm
Revolution per second _____
_____

RESULTS: Minimum Temperature in Glass _____ °C

Plum Drinks from Japan

Dr. Kazuhiko Kinosita, Professor of Biology at Kelo University, Yokohama, Japan provided the following recipes by translating popular Japanese recipes printed on bags of crystal sugar, called "ice sugar." Dr. Kinosita sent Chaos several bags of this sugar so she could try out his recipes using Rocky Mountain fruit.

Plum Wine

INGREDIENTS

1 kg crystal sugar
1 kg fresh plum (Japanese apricot)

1.8 liter white liquor

1. Wash plums and wipe off water. Put into a bottle in the order of plum, sugar and liquor.

2. Keep in a cold, dark place. Good after 2-3 months; best after 1-2 years.

Note: Addition of apricot kernels (or plum pits) will enhance the aroma.

Plum Syrup

INGREDIENTS

1 1.5 kg crystal sugar
1 kg plum

100-200 ml white liquor

1, Wash plums and remove water; put into a bottle, plum and sugar, forming layers of 1/3 of sugar, and 1/3 of plum.

2. Add liquor; wait for 2-3 weeks; transfer into a different bottle and keep refrigerated.

3. Dilute 3 to 4 times with cold water or carbonated water or mix with liquor to make a cocktail or make jelly.

"Ume-shu" Japanese Plum Liquor

Contributed by Junko Matsuda, tasted by Satoshi Matsuda,
Kyoto University, Kyoto, Japan

INGREDIENTS

1 kg fresh unripe (green) plums
500-800 grams sugar

1.8 litter "shou-chuu" 35% ALC
Japanese white liquor made from
yam/sweet potato

1. Wash each plum, cut in half and remove pit. Drain well on paper towels.

2. Put plums and sugar in layers alternately in a bottle. Then add shou-chuu slowly. Cap the bottle tightly.

3. Shake the bottle gently once a week or so for melting sugar. Keep it in a cool, dark place.

4. This will become an amber-colored, transparent liquor in 2 to 3 months.

5. Strain the liquor and drink it on the rocks or mixed with water. The plums can be eaten also.

Sima Mead

Chaos was recently in Helsinki where she was given a number of recipes by
Dr. Risto Orava and is wife. Dr. Orava is Professor of Physics at
the University of Helsinki

INGREDIENTS

5 liters of water
2 lemons
1/4 kg granulated sugar
1/4 kg brown sugar

1/2 liter sugar syrup
1 t yeast
1 bottle of beer
1 lb of raisins

1. Divide raisins and granulated sugar into two or more bottles.

2. Remove lemon rinds with potato peeler, then remove the white layer and cut the lemons into slices. Place the lemon slices and brown sugar in a large bowl.

3. Boil the water and pour it over the lemon slices and sugar. Let the mixture cool and add all the other ingredients including the yeast, dissolved in a bit of the liquid.

4. Let the mead ferment at room temperature overnight then pour through a sieve into the bottles which already have the granulated sugar and raisins in them.

5. Cork the bottles and keep them at room temperature for a few hours after which they should be put in a cool dark place. The drink is ready to serve after a few days but will be better if left for a week.

Sour Drinks
Strawberry or Apple

Dr, K. Kinosita, Kelo University, Yokohama, Japan
These sour drinks are to be diluted 3 to 4 times with cold water
or carbonated water.

INGREDIENTS

Strawberries   1 kg crystal sugar
1 kg fresh strawberries   900 ml of Japanese rice wine vinegar

1. Wash strawberries and remove calyxes and rotten parts.

2. Put ingredients into a bottle and wait for one week.

INGREDIENTS

Apples   1 kg crystal sugar
1 kg fresh apples   900 ml of Japanese rice wine vinegar

1. Wash apples and remove water.

2. Cut into pieces without peeling off the skin; remove the cores; cut into 5mm cubes

3. Put ingredients into a bottle and stir once a day; good after one week.

WEIGHTS
AND
MEASURES

Conversion Chart
Volume, Weight and Temperature Equivalent

American	Metric
¼ t	1.25 ml
½ t	2.5 ml
1 t	5 ml
½ T (1 ½ t)	7.5 ml
1 T (3 t)	15 ml
¼ cup (4T)	60 ml
1/3 cup (5T)	75 ml
½ cup (8T)	125 ml
2/3 cup (10T)_	150 ml
¾ cup (12T)	175 ml
1 cup (16T)	250 ml
1 ¼ cup	300 ml
1 ½ cup	350 ml
1 pint (2 cups)	500 ml
1 quart (4 cups)	1 liter

Avoirdupois	Metric
¼ oz	7 gm
½ oz	15 gm
1 oz	30 gm
2 oz	60 gm
3 oz	90 gm
4 oz	115 gm

Oven Temperatures

Fahrenheit	Celsius
200 °	100
225°	110
250°	130
275°	140
300°	150
325°	170
350°	180
375°	190
400°	200
425°	220
450°	230

Avoirdupois	Metric
5 oz	150 gm
6 oz	175 gm
7 oz	200 gm
8 oz	225 gm
9 oz	250 gm
10 oz	300 gm
11 oz	325 gm
12 oz	350 gm
13 oz	375 gm
14 oz	400 gm
15 oz	425 gm
1 lb	450 gm
1 lb. 2 oz	500 gm
1 ½ lb	750 gm
2 lb	900 gm
2 ¼ lb	1 Kg
3 lb	1.4 Kg
4 lb	1.8 Kg

Oven Temperatures

Oven	Fahrenheit	Celsius
Very Cool	250-275	130-140
Cool	300	150
Warm	325	170
Moderate	350	180
Moderately Hot	375	190
	400	200
Hot	425	220
Very Hot	450	230
	475	250

Sky-High Baking Tips

If you live more than 3,000 feet above sea level, you know what the air is like up there — thin. The decrease in air pressure means adjustments need to be made in baking times, temperatures, and in some ingredients.

- When baking a cake above 3,000 feet, increase the oven temperature by 25 degrees.

- As altitude increases, yeast breads tend to rise more rapidly. To develop their flavor fully, allow the dough to rise twice until doubled in bulk, punching down dough after each rising.

- Use the chart below for adjustments of ingredients.

At 3,000 feet:
Sugar: for each cup, decrease 1-3 teaspoons
Liquid: for each cup, add 1-2 tablespoons
Baking Powder: for each teaspoon, decrease 1/8 teaspoon

At 5,000 feet:
Sugar: for each cup, decrease 1-2 tablespoons
Liquid: for each cup, add 2-4 tablespoons
Baking Powder: for each teaspoon, decrease 1/8 to 1/4 teaspoon

At 7,000 feet:
Sugar: for each cup decrease 1-1/2 to 3 tablespoons
Liquid: for each cup, add 3-4 tablespoons
Baking Powder: for each teaspoons, decrease 1/4 teaspoon

At 10,000 feet:
Sugar: for each cup, decrease 2 to 3-1/2 tablespoons
Liquid: for each cup, add 3-4 tablespoons
Baking Powder: for each teaspoon, decrease 1/4 to 1/2 teaspoons

A COOKED BOOK

THE END

INDEX